A Collector's Zeal:
Treasures from the
DeCoursey Fales Collection
at Manhattan College

A Collector's Zeal:
Treasures from the
DeCoursey Fales Collection
at Manhattan College

TIMOTHY G. GRESS

MANHATTAN COLLEGE

Riverdale, New York

2020

ISBN-13: 978-0-692-15009-2

Contents

MAJOR JOHN ANDRÉ,

Adjutant General to his Majesty's Forces in North America under the Command of Sir Henry Clinton.

Engraved portrait (1784) of Major John Andre, inserted by an early owner as a frontispiece to vol. 4 of an extra-illustrated copy of the *Letters of Anna Seward* (Edinburgh: Printed by George Ramsay for Archibald Constable & Co. [and 3 others], 1811).

Foreword

The DeCoursey Fales Collection at Manhattan College is a remarkable collection of eighteenth-, nineteenth-, and early twentieth-century literature and ephemera in a surprising place, the library of a small, Catholic liberal arts college known not for research but for its student focus. Built by Fales out of his friendship with Brother Albert Paul Gladhill, FSC, the curator of rare books at Manhattan College in the 1960s, from the surplus of the larger New York University Fales Library, the Manhattan College Fales Collection offers a kaleidoscopic, multi-paned window into the history of the novel, eighteenth- and nineteenth-century print culture, and twentieth-century collecting practices.

Fales's uniquely open-minded attitude toward collecting led him voraciously to accumulate materials regardless of their supposed "literary" status, valuing instead all literature as representative of its moment. Because of this, he created a collection that offers both breadth and depth. One can study, for example, a single year in the collection and understand the reading tastes of that moment. Or one can pursue a genre such as the Gothic novel or detective fiction in its many historical forms. The collection also provides distinctive teaching opportunities to expose students to first editions or Victorian three-deckers and to foster love of the material artifact. It offers scholars even more, placing the works of Charles Dickens or Walter Scott in tandem with lesser-known works like those of William Harrison Ainsworth (first edition of *Jack Sheppard*, 1839) or Elizabeth Inchbald (first edition of *A Simple Story*, 1791). As just one instance of the possibilities these riches hold, imagine finding, as I did, when I began my own work on Anna Seward, that the Manhattan College library has the rare six-volume first edition of her *Letters* (1811)! Or uncovering, as Tim Gress ('19), New York University graduate student in English and author of this pamphlet, did: a first edition of *The Refugee*, a reprinting of Herman Melville's novel *Israel Potter* (1855) that inspired outrage in Melville due to the title change.

Tim Gress's undergraduate work at the library and in his Branigan Research project, directed by President Brennan O'Donnell and me, recovering and restoring this collection of more than 3,000 works, unearthed treasures we didn't even know we had. And there is much more to excavate. Tim's passion for books has reanimated a corpus that promises a whole new corps of stories. No other Catholic college offers this wealth of resources in the eighteenth- and nineteenth-century novel, ripe for scholarly endeavor. We invite you to visit and explore.

Ashley Cross
Professor of English
Manhattan College

DeCoursey Fales, painted in 1919 by Lydia Field Emmett. From *The Fales Family of Bristol, Rhode Island*, by DeCoursey Fales (Privately printed, 1919).

A Collector's Zeal

What we have loved,
Others will love, and we will teach them how.

—William Wordsworth to Samuel Taylor Coleridge,
The Prelude (1850)

By building distinctive book collections and placing them in reach of students and scholars, DeCoursey Fales (1888–1966) taught readers to love the novel in all its depth and breadth. An avid collector of literary first editions, manuscripts, letters, and ephemera, Fales used his private wealth to translate his personal love for books into a public good for the benefit of students and scholars in New York and elsewhere. Much as his father Haliburton had inspired him to love literature, he believed he could instill the same passion in young people and rekindle new love in seasoned scholars.

Fales's goal was to document the history and development of the novel as we know it today. At a time when the novel was still not valued as a worthy subject of academic study or as a collectible item, Fales was a pioneer in collecting both "important" works, many of which were available only for high sums at auction, and lesser-known works that others might have cast aside.

For Fales, this approach to book collecting was not empty rhetoric; it was a way of life. He began sending literary works to the New York Public Library and the Morgan Library & Museum in 1952. Although he had graduated from Harvard & Columbia, Fales chose New York University and Manhattan College as his primary beneficiaries, donating books to their libraries from 1957 (NYU) and 1961 (Manhattan) onward.

The Manhattan College Fales Collection includes British and American literature from the early eighteenth century to the mid-twentieth century.[1] With 250 years of the written word represented in more than 3,000 volumes, the Collection is especially strong in its holdings of Romantic, Victorian, and Edwardian literature, primarily fiction, and in twentieth-century crime fiction. The nineteenth-century English fiction collection is among the best of any Catholic institution of higher learning, and the Fales Collection contains works that cannot be found even in some of the country's foremost research libraries.

DeCoursey Fales

DeCoursey Fales, known as The Commodore in his later life, was born June 1, 1888, in Saranac Lake, New York. Following his early education at St. Paul's School, Fales enrolled at Harvard University and completed his studies there in 1911.[2] His passion for literature was clear at the age of ten, when he became "enamored with *A Brief History of the United States*, by A.S. Barnes."[3] Fales described his love for books as "a lifetime enthusiasm,"[4] and he read widely in his father's library, which was especially rich in the works of Sir Walter Scott.[5] A reputed kinsman of De-Coursey's father, Scott remained central to Fales's collecting activities for the rest of his life.

Along with the works of Scott, Fales read and began to collect countless novels about the Civil War, along with adventure stories and mysteries—stories of "King Brady, Nick Carter, and Pluck and Luck."[6] However, it was Fales's love of Scott's Waverley novels from which he "derived his interest in the novel as a work of art, an interest [that] governed the formation of his collection of rare books."[7]

Fales's years at Harvard had a transformative effect, giving him the background and understanding to become a discerning collector and student of literature. At Harvard, Fales took two courses in literature. The first, taught by Professor Charles Copeland Townsend, focused primarily on the writings of Samuel Johnson and his literary circle. Here, Fales was introduced to the likes of David Garrick, Joshua Reynolds, Hester Lynch Piozzi, Joseph Barretti, Henry Thrale, Fanny Burney, Oliver Goldsmith, and James Boswell.[8]

The most important event in Fales's development as a collector was his second course in literature titled: "History and Development of the English Novel," taught by Professor Bliss Perry. One of the first academics to teach fiction as a serious literary form, Perry was already noted for his scholarly work—in particular, for *A Study of Prose Fiction* (1902).[9] In his teaching, Perry "advocated a broad-ranging approach to the novel that took into account both the entertainment and aesthetic value of the form."[10] After outlining earlier works of French and Spanish literature, the course focused on authors such as Tobias Smollett, Henry Fielding, Laurence Sterne, and, again, Oliver Goldsmith. Perry also "touch[ed] upon the Gothic Novel—[Sir Walter] Scott and the early Victorians—with lectures on [Charles] Dickens and [William Makepeace] Thackeray—[Anthony] Trollope and [Thomas] Hardy."[11] Along with Sir Walter Scott, the authors covered in Perry's course became some of Fales's favorites. Looking back on the course, Fales exclaimed, "Now I was caught by a love of the standard novel and with a mind inquiring after who were and are the great novelists."[12]

Following Harvard, Fales went on a six-month tour of Europe with his father, then returned to New York to enroll at Columbia University Law School. He became "lost in [his] law books" and earned his law degree in 1914.[13] Then came World War I, from which Fales emerged a decorated naval veteran—and a lover of tales of the sea, both fact and fiction, as can be seen in his collection. After the War, Fales returned to his wife Dorothy and their young son Haliburton, and went to work at the law firm of Cadwalader, Wickersham, and Taft. In 1941 he left the legal field to become president of the New York Bank for Savings and, after his retirement in 1957, chairman of the board.[14]

Fales had a lifelong passion for sailing. He won the Newport-to-Bermuda yacht race in 1962 and was commodore of the New York Yacht Club. He also served as chairman of the Advisory Committee on Sailing of the United States Naval Academy.[15]

A Unique Approach to Collecting

Although he had been collecting since he was a young boy, Fales first devised a coherent plan for his efforts in 1926. He recalled the formative moment in his *Confessions of a Book-Collector*:

> In the winter of 1926, I read all the novels and poems of Sir Walter Scott. Now I was in trouble.... Here I was thinking of Sir Walter—histories of faraway countries and lands—the Hebrides, the Crusades and, above all, the novel and Bliss Perry and his development of the novel. Yes! There

was no doubt about it; I was going to collect the
novel.[16]

His grand scope—"to collect *all* of the novelists—American and British"—from the eighteenth to the twentieth
century, including all historical developments and subgenres, was something that few, if any, collectors had
taken on before.[17] There were collectors who specialized
in specific genres and time periods, such as Morris L. Parrish and Clifton Waller Barrett—but few, if any, had ever
aspired to take on such an ambitious and demanding
task. Early on, Fales was discouraged from taking on
such a large project by his friend E. Hubert Litchfield,
who himself owned a fantastic collection of first editions
(some of which are now at Manhattan College). According to Fales, "Mr. Litchfield told me off. There was too
much to collect; if I pursued the novel and novelists—all
of them and in depth. I was wrong; I should be discouraged. There was not even room."[18] Fales, with a "glint in
his eye," was not discouraged, however.[19] He recounted
his early passion in later years when he stated, "You
might envision me at the top of a rickety ladder balancing
my Merle Johnson in one hand and a copy of one of
[Henry] James' novels in the other to see if it checked on
all points."[20]

Ultimately, Fales hoped to build "the best collection
in depth of the novelists in question, from 1740 to the present [1960] and all of the minor supporting biographies,
articles, and essays, as well as the first, second, and third-
class novels."[21] In order to fulfill such great ambitions,
Fales had to devise a concrete plan. Had he stepped out-
side of his precise collecting roadmap, he would surely
have been overtaken by a sense of bibliomania and not

been able to complete his goal. The plan that Fales devised was this: "I would start out with Sir Walter Scott and work slowly backwards from him and then later forward again."[22] Scott, serving as a bridge between the Romantic and Victorian periods, became the nucleus of a collection that moved in two different directions—"forward through the nineteenth and to the twentieth century, backward to the eighteenth-century novelists and to many of their predecessors—the chroniclers, the pamphleteers, and the playwrights."[23]

Remembering the undergraduate course he had taken almost two decades earlier, Fales began to collect first editions of novels by the authors Perry had taught—Dickens, Trollope, Thackeray, and Scott. Rather than collecting all the subsequent editions of works by well-known authors, Fales collected "in depth," a term that, in his vocabulary, meant "assembling, along with an author's major works, a sufficient amount of his secondary and supplementary material to present a rounded portrait of the whole [author] and the whole mind."[24] He then branched out further, collecting works by and about each author's literary circle, and he eventually expanded his scope to include the lesser-known authors and genres of the Romantic and Victorian periods.

Backtracking through the eighteenth century to the novelists that influenced Scott—Daniel Defoe, Smollett, and Fielding—Fales went even further back: to Raphael Holinshed's *Chronicles of England, Scotland, and Ireland* (1577), which, as he knew, contained vital historical context relating to the English narrative tradition. He also acquired an outstanding collection of the seventeenth-century author Aphra Behn and her early works, such as the novel *Oroonoko* (1688).[25]

Additionally, Fales collected American authors, based partly on his love for Scott (and the American piracies of Scott's novels) and partly on Perry's interest in the differences between British and American literature.[26] Fales eventually amassed an impressive collection of writers such as Charles Brockden Brown and James Fenimore Cooper. His large-scale interest in collecting American literature did not emerge until later, however, around 1959—two years after his initial donation to New York University. Fales decided that he would collect all the authors listed in Merle Johnson's definitive *American First Editions*, a comprehensive checklist of the complete works and ephemeral publications of nearly two-hundred canonical and non-canonical American authors through 1942.[27] He "toured all the stores on [fourth] avenue for a whole winter and on to the next. I followed with Hawthorne, Holmes, Longfellow. I travelled once a year to Boston to visit Goodspeed's, Morvill's and other stores. My theory was: Catch the books one by one. I needed to fill the lists."[28] And fill the lists he did! More than 500 of the volumes included in Johnson's bibliography can be found in the Fales Collection—all this and more in only seven years' time.

After focusing on the novels of the nineteenth and earlier centuries, Fales shifted his attention to the twentieth-century classics and the lesser-known fields of Irish and Scottish literature. He was not interested only in historical works, however; he also avidly acquired contemporary titles, relying on Lyle Wright's bibliographical checklist *American Fiction* and focusing specifically on detective fiction and African-American fiction.[29] One of the earliest collectors of African-American literature, Fales acquired nearly all the volumes listed in

Maxwell Whiteman's *A Century of Fiction by American Negroes*, including works by Charles Chesnutt, James Baldwin, and Richard Wright, most notably the first edition of *Native Son* (1940). All these have made their way into the Fales Collection at Manhattan College.

Fales was also interested in Gothic novels of horror and suspense, many of which are now difficult to acquire due to their rarity. The Gothic novel, represented in the Fales Collection through the works of authors such as Jane Porter, Clara Reeve, and William Beckford, laid a foundation for the contemporary detective novels that Fales also acquired. The detective genre, perhaps best represented at Manhattan College in twenty-eight works by Agatha Christie, paved the way for the tales of mystery and horror that we know today.[30]

Finally, Fales understood that works in other genres could help readers gain a broader perspective on the novel. As he stated,

> I was interested in the telling of a story. Before the novel, as we know it, stories were told in many forms, and in many periods of literature in the past plays and poetry were the chief vehicles for storytelling.... The plays and poetry in this collection serve as a background to the main theme, which is the novel.[31]

Fales did not simply collect an author's best-well known works in first edition, as many collectors did. He "sought first appearances in periodicals, dramatizations and imitations of the author's work, and critical biographical, and bibliographical material."[32] He wanted to help readers gain a complete picture of each novelist, and this meant he was interested in everything they wrote—even a brief Introduction. From the 1920s onward, Fales's collection grew to encompass thousands of volumes that represented nearly every genre, subgenre, and period of literature from the eighteenth century onward. Most of the volumes were packed into the Fales family home in Gladstone, New Jersey. Running out of space, Fales was faced with a difficult question: What am I to do with my collection?

The Fales Collection at Manhattan College

Enlisting the help of friend and trusted dealer David Kirschenbaum, founder of the Carnegie Book Shop, Fales set out to find an institution that would keep his library together as one distinct entity. Kirschenbaum proposed that Fales find a local institution "willing to accept his collection with the stipulation that adequate quarters be provided to keep it intact."[33] That institution was New York University. "Remembering his father's youth in Washington Square, and with the encouragement of Gordan N. Ray, New York University faculty member, collector, and fellow member of the prestigious Grolier Club for book collectors," Fales accepted President Carroll Vincent Newsom's offer. Much of Fales's personal collection was donated to NYU on December 18, 1957.[34] At the time, Dr. Ernest Hettich, director of the university libraries, proudly declared that the Fales donation would "put NYU library on the map."[35]

NYU received not just a fantastic collection, but the collector himself. As Fales put it, he worked with the University as "'librarian in charge of acquisitions' for a fine rare book collection housed, as I think it should be, in an academic community."[36] Originally, the Fales Library at NYU included about eight thousand books and four thousand letters and manuscripts. By 1963, through Fales's continued zeal as chief buyer, it had grown to fifty thousand books and twelve thousand letters and manuscripts.

With an academic community behind him, Fales took to the rare book market in ways never seen before. As he joyfully expressed, "now I am no longer collecting for myself but for the library of a great university and, strongly enough, I find that I tackle the job with tenfold more zeal than I had when I was buying books for myself. And this is a most exciting realization."[37]   He further noted,

> I receive every day, except Saturday and Sunday, catalogues from booksellers in Canada, England, and the United States. There is hardly a day that I do not read these catalogues as soon and as fast as I am able on their receipt. That very day I must get off a special air mail to England or other faraway places. I must phone or cable to outwit some great collector who operates faster than I. My problem here is how to avoid duplication and not be satisfied with second best.[38]

John T. Winterich, who worked closely with Fales at NYU, commented that "no great book collection in the United States, or probably in all the world, is growing, or ever has grown, at such a prodigious rate as the Fales."[39] Unfortunately, this rapid expansion meant that the Fales Library was quickly outgrowing its original space. Manhattan College was the solution to the problem.

By early 1961, with shelf space at a premium, Fales turned back to his friend and trusted dealer David Kirshenbaum. For many years, Kirshenbaum had been an important consultant to Brother Albert Paul Gladhill,

FSC, the curator of rare books at Manhattan College. Kirshenbaum, whose reputation as a matchmaker had already been demonstrated in 1957, put Fales and Brother Paul in contact with each other. Brother Paul's reputation for maintaining and expanding a superb collection of rare sixteenth- and seventeenth-century materials made him the person Fales was looking for—one who would give his extra copies a home and maintain them as a distinct collection in the service of higher education.

The books that would make up the Fales Collection at Manhattan College came from the Fales Library in four major installments—684 volumes in 1961, 499 volumes in 1962, 252 volumes in 1963, and more than 196 volumes in 1966. Although Fales was planning to donate 30,000 volumes to the College, illness intervened. In the end, the Fales Collection reached a size of more than 4,000 volumes.[40]

When Fales was awarded an honorary doctorate at the 1966 Commencement ceremonies, he proclaimed that he was "especially pleased to have been of help to the students of Manhattan College."[41] His legacy has persisted to the present day. For nearly sixty years, the Fales Collection has fulfilled the purpose he outlined, as a source of knowledge and inspiration to countless "students of the novel."

Notes

1. The books held by New York University are the *Fales Library*. Those held by Manhattan College are the *Fales Collection*.
2. Taylor & Kelly, p. 5.
3. Fales, p. 1. Except as noted, all bibliographic references to *Fales* refer to *Confessions of a Book Collector* (privately printed, 1960).
4. New York University, *Bulletin*, Society for the Libraries, Winter 1959.
5. Ibid.
6. Fales, p. 2.
7. New York University, *Bulletin*, Society for the Libraries, Winter 1959.
8. Fales, p. 2.
9. Fales, p. 2; Perry.
10. Taylor & Kelly, p. 5.
11. Fales, p. 3.
12. Ibid.
13. Ibid.
14. Ibid.
15. Taylor & Kelly, p. 6.
16. Fales, p. 3.
17. Ibid.
18. Fales, p. 4.
19. Fales, p. 7.
20. Fales, p. 7. "Merle Johnson" refers to *Merle Johnson's American First Editions*.
21. Fales, p. 8.
22. Fales, p. 4.
23. Egerer, *DeCoursey Fales*, p. 2
24. Winterich, *An Appreciation*, p. 7; Taylor & Kelly, p. 6.
25. Taylor & Kelly, p. 6.
26. Ibid.
27. Fales, p. 7.
28. Ibid.
29. Taylor & Kelly, p. 6; Wright, *American Fiction, 1774–1850*; *1851–1875*; and *1876–1900*.
30. Taylor & Kelly, p. 6.

31. Ibid.
32. Egerer, "Fales Library," p. 1.
33. Basbanes, p. 41.
34. Taylor & Kelly, p. 7.
35. New York University, "Dinner for DeCoursey Fales."
36. Winterich, *A Record of Growth*, p. 5.
37. Ibid.
38. Fales, p. 8.
39. Winterich, *A Record of Growth*, p. 10.
40. Manhattan College, *Cardinal Hayes Library Annual Report*, 1976–1977 and prior years.
41. DeCoursey Fales, letter to Brother Paul Gladhill, Mar. 31, 1966.

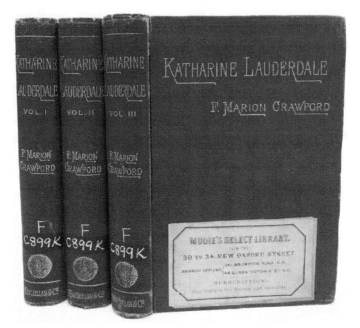

Katharine Lauderdale, by Francis Marion Crawford,
a three-decker once owned by Mudie's Select Library (London and New York: Macmillan & Co.,
1894).

Research Value of the Fales Collection

Mr. Fales's goal is to provide as complete a picture of an author, a period, a field as a collector's
zeal can make it. There are great first editions
and also odd bits of a particular writer, ephemera that lends vitality and richness.

—*The New York Times*, 1963

This essay evaluates the influence and legacy of Fales on
the fields of literature and book collecting—a legacy that
has long been overlooked—and critically assesses the
Manhattan College Fales Collection in relationship to the
much larger Fales Library at New York University. It
shows how Fales's prescient efforts have built collections
that are essential to the study of the history of the novel
in English.

Highways and Byways

The most important aspect of Fales's collecting process
was his foresight in collecting not just well-known and canonical authors, but those once regarded as "minor" by
collectors and scholars. Arguably, he was most interested
in acquiring the works that the everyday person was
reading—works that showcased the development, in content and in physical format, of narrative fiction in the
eighteenth, nineteen, and twentieth centuries. In other
words, Fales attempted to collect works which represented the full range of published novelists during this

300-year period, regardless of their gender, race, or position in society. He was, in his own words, "dedicated to collecting all worthwhile novelists in depth."[1]

To a large extent, his contemporaries focused their energies on identifying major authors thorough bibliographies and check-lists such as A. Edward Newton's "One Hundred Good Novels" and Merle Johnson's *High Spots of American Literature* (1929).[2] In contrast, Fales sought to acquire what he referred to as "the first, second, and third-class novels."[3] Fales was informed by contemporary bibliographies, but he also moved beyond them. He felt that many of the writers not yet adopted into the literary canon were just as important as those celebrated in literary circles. He also believed it was important to preserve their works in the format in which they had first been presented to the public—in serialized parts, for instance, or in multiple cloth volumes.

The theorist Terry Eagleton has commented on the role that literary value judgments play in determining which authors and books are taught in the classroom:

> Value-judgments would certainly seem to have a lot to do with what is judged literature and what isn't—not necessarily in the sense that writing has to be "fine" to be literary, but that it has to be *of the kind* that is judged fine: it may be an inferior example of a generally valued mode. Nobody would bother to say that a bus ticket was an example of inferior literature, but someone might say that the poetry of Ernest Dowson was.[4]

Collectors and scholars of the early twentieth century were quick to judge and dismiss less critically acclaimed authors—*inferior examples* of the types of "fine" literature described by Eagleton. Rejecting this view, Fales saw all writers of prose as potentially important literary figures who had something to offer the study of literature. If they were widely read, or especially interesting for one reason or another, they were judged worthwhile additions to his collection. Fales was a visionary in this respect and, by valuing these authors and their works decades before most literary critics did, he made later scholarly recovery work possible by preserving the works of writers such as Dowson. A key player in the *fin de siècle*, Dowson is well represented in the Fales Collection, and in this guide.

Arthur Swann, head of Parke-Bennet galleries, once observed of the Fales Library, "It's not [just] the highways…. It's the byways, too."[5] "Byway" authors are invaluable for the comprehensive study of trends, genres, or literary periods, partly in their own right but partly as those with whom the "highway" authors were involved. For example, the works of Maria Edgeworth—a "byway" novelist from the perspective of Swann and other mid-century collectors and scholars—can be found in the Fales Collection due to their influence on Sir Walter Scott. From Scott's point of view, "they [Edgeworth and Jane Austen] were truly the novelists of their times—the customs, the incidents and happenstances and dialogues of their eras—which they faithfully and artistically put forward as true national pictures."[6] While Edgeworth may not have held the same favorable reputation as other Romantic writers during the twentieth century, her writings had a profound effect on her contemporary Scott. She now receives considerable scholarly attention, largely due to recovery work undertaken with collections such as the Fales Collection. For instance, a search in the MLA International database shows a wealth of recent scholarship on Edgeworth—559 references to Edgeworth (as of March

2020), including more than 300 since 2000. Once considered mere "byway" authors, novelists such as Edgeworth have become central players in literary scholarship. Always prescient in his methods of collecting, Fales has opened up new avenues for literary criticism and study.

John T. Winterich has noted that "A minor author, however unimportant he or she may seem in perspective, may be important because he initiated a trend—was in a small way a pioneer."[7] Edgeworth established the genre of the regional novel, thereby influencing Scott and other authors throughout the nineteenth century. For that reason, scholars now recognize Edgeworth as more than a minor author, a status that confirms Fales's insightful description of her in 1960 as the "smallest giant of her era."[8] We know now what Fales knew then: students of the Romantic movement cannot fully understand major authors such as Sir Walter Scott, Robert Southey, and William Wordsworth, all represented in the Fales Collection, without undertaking a study of the works of Maria Edgeworth, whose work engaged all these notable writers. In fact, studying Edgeworth shifts our understanding of these male writers and may even decenter their position in the literary canon. The Fales Collection allows us to view Edgeworth and others as Fales would have wanted—as worthwhile figures essential to our understanding of literary history.

Books as Material Artifacts

"Byway" authors may have been popular in their time, but in most cases their popularity was short-lived. Their books were usually printed just once, and first editions are not easy to locate in libraries or online. Even when these authors' works are available online, the unique "thingness" of the books themselves, as physical objects with tangible properties that mediate the relationship between reader and author, provides a valuable and essential window into book history and print culture.

These material qualities cannot be duplicated virtually, and the physical characteristics of each volume often provide valuable information on the history of the novel. For instance, *Katharine Lauderdale,* by F. Marion Crawford, was one of the last of the Victorian three-deckers (three-volume novels) produced, and the physical volumes reveal how such works were encountered by nineteenth-century readers. Our copy was previously owned by Mudie's Select Library, a lending library that was remarkably successful both as a business venture and as a means of bringing popular literature to middle-class families; it was once the largest circulating library in England. The volumes in the Fales Collection bear the yellow labels that marked them as part of Mudie's Library, and these very volumes were most likely read by dozens of Mudie's subscribers who could not wait to get their hands on them.

Even when they duplicate titles held by the Fales Library at NYU, the volumes at Manhattan College differ in their physical characteristics—in the stories they tell. These books have unique markings, inscriptions, bookplates, bindings, and even smells that reflect their histories as physical artifacts. For instance, one of NYU's copies of Samuel Johnson's *Lives of the Most Eminent English Poets* (1781) was a gift from Albert Lewin to the University; it was never acquired by Fales and cannot be linked to his personal collection or his collection-building activities. In contrast, the copy at Manhattan College can be traced from London, where it was printed, to Ireland, the home of its first owner, to the Carnegie Book Shop, where it was purchased by Fales; and then to Gladstone, New Jersey where he held it in his hands and personally added it to his shelf.

Notes

1. Fales, p. 9.
2. "One Hundred Good Novels" is included in Newton's *This Book Collecting Game* (Little, Brown, & Co., 1928).
3. Fales, p. 8.
4. Eagleton, p. 9.
5. Winterich, *An Appreciation*, p. 10.
6. Fales, p. 6.
7. Winterich, *An Appreciation*, p. 10.
8. Fales, p. 6.

Frontispiece of *Ten Nights in a Bar Room,* by Timothy Shay Arthur (Boston: L.P. Crown & Co.; Philadelphia: J.W. Bradley, 1854.)

Treasures from the Collection

In his 1968 *Sir Walter Scott in the Fales Library* (p. 2), Edgar Johnson declared,

> Not only New York University, but the entire scholarly world, is indebted to DeCoursey Fales for the generosity and the lifelong dedication to literature that has created this noble endowment not only for the study of Scott but, in fact, for the study of very large numbers of major and minor novelists and poets from the eighteenth-century to the current avant-garde.

Indeed, the Manhattan College community and the many visitors to the College are indebted to Fales for making this extraordinary collection available.

In the 150 entries presented here, I have tried to demonstrate the diversity and importance of the more than 3,000 volumes held within the Fales Collection: canonical as well as non-canonical authors, works that showcase the periods and movements in which they were written, and volumes once owned by notable individuals that, taken together, offer a broad, historical survey of the novel. The Collection allows us to immerse ourselves in "the telling of a story" and to understand both what people were reading and how they were able to engage with the text. By studying these texts in their original formats, we can better understand how the development, reception, and collecting of the novel have shaped the literary culture in which we live.

These 150 works were chosen due to their influence on the English and American novel and on the larger literary movements of which these authors were a part. My primary goal has been to highlight the "odd bits" of particular authors and periods, presenting both well-known authors and lesser-known authors who were representative of their times. With entries ranging in date from 1715 to 1964, the guide is divided into eight sections. Each section includes one or more subsections that highlight particular movements, groups, or genres that are well represented within the Fales Collection:

- 17th and 18th-century literature
    Gothic novels
- 19th-century British fiction
    Gothic novels
    Children's fiction
- 19th-century American fiction
    Regional tales
- Poetry and verse
    The Fireside Poets
- Nonfiction
    Biography
- Drama
    Comedy
- 20th-century British fiction
    Crime and detective fiction
- 20th-century American fiction
    The short story

Most authors appear only once, although a few—such as Samuel Johnson, who seems to have had his hand in half of London's literary output at the end of the eighteenth century—are represented through more than one work.

Each entry presents information on the author and content of the work, along with bibliographic information relating to imprint, status of publication, binding, and any features specific to the volumes owned by Manhattan College (e.g., bookplates). (Some of this information has been abridged due to space constraints.) The additional works mentioned within each entry, unless otherwise noted, are not part of the Fales Collection.

In the text describing each work, quotations without attribution are from the work itself. Other quotations are attributed, and each entry concludes with references to additional bibliographies or reference works where the title is mentioned. These bibliographies often cover specific literary movements, time periods, or authors, and some, such as *American First Editions*, were used by Fales to select volumes for his collection.

The works cited in the bibliographic entries are listed on pages 117–131. For multi-volume reference works, Roman numerals indicate the volume. Several standard bibliographies are indicated by abbreviated titles:

- American Firsts: Blanck, *Merle Johnson's American First Editions*

- ANB: Oxford University Press, *American National Biography*

- BAL: Blanck, *Bibliography of American Literature*

- Beinecke: McKay, *A Stevenson Library*

- DNB: Oxford University Press, *Dictionary of National Biography*

- ESTC: British Library, *English Short Title Catalogue*

- Grolier American: Grolier Club, *One Hundred Influential American Books Printed Before 1900*

- Grolier English: Grolier Club, *One Hundred Books Famous in English Literature*
- High Spots: Johnson, *High Spots of American Literature*
- NCBEL: Watson, *New Cambridge Bibliography of English Literature*
- Parley to Penrod: Blanck, *Peter Parley to Penrod*
- PW: *Publishers Weekly*
- Rothschild: Cambridge University Press, *The Rothschild Library*
- Sadleir: *XIX Century Fiction*
- Tinker: Metzdorf, *The Tinker Library*
- TLS: *Times Literary Supplement*.

Acknowledgments

I am grateful for the advice and assistance of William H. Walters, Charles Carter, and the staff of the Fales Library at New York University; for the copyediting of Laurin Paradise; for the almost inexhaustible resources of the New York Public Library; and for the support of Ashley Cross and Brennan O'Donnell, who have fostered my love for the Fales Collection and for the study of literature.

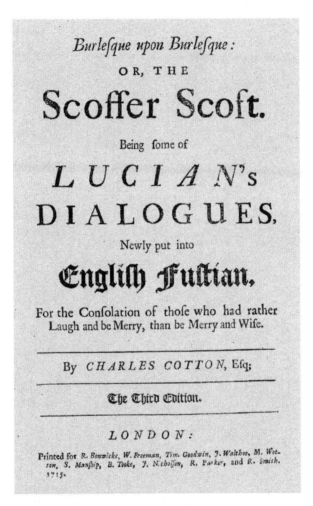

Title page of *Burlesque upon Burlesque: or, The Scoffer Scoft*, one of four works included in *The Genuine Works of Charles Cotton, Esq.* (London: Printed for R. Bonwicke [and 9 others], 1715).

17TH- AND 18TH-CENTURY LITERATURE

"Before the novel, as we know it," wrote Fales, "plays and poetry were the chief vehicles for storytelling" (New York University, *Bulletin*, Society for the Libraries, Winter 1959). It was not until the eighteenth century that the novel overtook drama and verse to become the chief vehicle of popular literary entertainment. Both fiction and nonfiction titles are shown here in an attempt to demonstrate the wide range of literary expression during the early stages of the modern novel's development. Of particular importance to this period is the Gothic novel. Gothic tales of horror and suspense, which began to emerge in the 1760s, later came to influence the development of crime and detective fiction as well as other related subgenres.

Baretti, Joseph. *A Journey from London to Genoa, Through England, Portugal, Spain, and France.* London: Printed for T. Davis & L. Davis, 1770. First ed., 4 vols. Full contemporary calf. This work, which chronicles Baretti's travels through Spain, Portugal, and France from 1761 to 1765, was suggested by friend and fellow critic Samuel Johnson. Baretti, an Italian by birth, writes in the preface that "[Johnson] exhorted me to write daily and with all possible minuteness: it was he that pointed out the topics which would most interest and most delight in a further publication" (Courtney, p. 99). ESTC t83926.

Blane, William. *Essays on Hunting. Containing a Philosophical Enquiry into the Nature and Properties of the Scent.* Southampton: Printed and sold by T. Baker; London: J. Robson and J. Fielding; Oxford: D. Prince, 1781. First ed. Half contemporary calf over marbled boards. Although Blane appears to have written nothing truly original, he was a "prolific producer of sporting books" (Higginson, *British and American*, p. 27, 404). *Essays on Hunting,* an extension of a rare pamphlet published by John Smallman Gardiner in 1750 entitled *The Art and Pleasures of Hare-Hunting,* also includes an account of the Vizier's manner of hunting in the Mogul Empire. It was Blane's hope that "many other lovers of the chase may be pleased with [this collection of essays]." ESTC t71428; NCBEL II 1560.

Cotton, Charles. *The Genuine Works of Charles Cotton, Esq.* London: Printed for R. Bonwicke [and 9 others], 1715. First collected ed. Full contemporary calf, Cambridge style. This miscellaneous collection of Cotton's most popular works, published posthumously, contains two burlesque poems, a treatise on horticulture and the satirical poem "The Wonders of the Peake," where Cotton features himself as a picaresque anti-hero. It is the oldest volume in the Fales Collection. Wordsworth, Coleridge, and Charles Lamb rediscovered Cotton—a highly respected poet, angler, and horticulturalist—as a poet of nature. DNB; ESTC t144429; NCBEL II 438.

Godwin, William. *The Enquirer. Reflections on Education, Manners, and Literature.* London: Printed for G.G. & J. Robinson, 1797. First ed. Full contemporary calf (re-backed). In ink: "Croydon's Library Teignmouth." Ink ownership stamp: "John A. Cockburn." The political philosopher Godwin was at work on this collection of essays during his romance with the feminist thinker Mary Wollstonecraft, and while she was pregnant with their first child Mary, who would later pen the infamous novel *Frankenstein* (1818). Many of the essays deal with psychological aspects of child-rearing and the formation of the child's character. ESTC t94276; NCBEL II 1250; Rothschild 1018.

Johnson, Samuel. *A Dictionary of the English Language. Abstracted from the Folio Edition.* London: Printed for J. Knapton [and 4 others], 1756. First abridged ed., 2 vols, with the phrase "by the author." Full contemporary calf. In ink: "B.P. Baffard 1758." Although "the quotations are omitted, the explanations are abridged and a great number of the words are left out" (Courtney, p. 62), the abridged version, retailing at 10 shillings, was the first a general reader could afford. As a result, the *Dictionary* sold over a thousand copies a year for the next thirty years—cementing its reputation as what was then the definitive English language dictionary. ESTC t083957; Fleeman 56.1DA/1; NCBEL II 1130.

Johnson, Samuel. *The Lives of the Most Eminent English Poets: With Critical Observations on their Works.* London: Printed for C. Bathurst [and 35 others], 1781. Second ed., 4 vols. Full contemporary tree calf. Book-label and ink signature of Eliza Viscountess Galway. First published between 1779 and 1781, these short biographies and critical appraisals of 52 poets set a new standard for English literary biography. An early London review stated, "We believe few people will be found so depraved in their judgment, or so devoid of literary taste as to deny that these lives contain a rich fund of sublime entertainment" (*London Magazine: Or, Gentleman's Monthly Intelligencer,* Dec. 1781, p. 593). Courtney, pp. 141–142; ESTC t146734; Fleeman 79.4LP/5; NCBEL II 1130; Rothschild 1265; Tinker 1365.

Johnstone, Charles. *The Reverie: or, A Flight to the Paradise of Fools.* London: Printed for T. Beckett & P.A. da [*sic*] Hondt, 1763. First authorized ed., 2 vols. Full contemporary speckled calf. Johnstone was best known during his lifetime for *Chrysal, or the Adventures of a Guinea* (1760). *The Reverie* is his second published work. A political satire attacking Lord Bute, Prime Minister under George III, and other prominent political figures of the day, the storyteller is in a reverie (or daydream) and "recounts various events and philosophical thoughts that occur to him" (Loeber & Loeber J45). Block, p. 124; ESTC t126192; NCBEL II 1000; Raven 724.

Kirkby, John. *The Capacity and Extent of the Human Under-standing; Exemplified in the Extraordinary Case of Automathes.* London: Printed for R. Manby & H. Shute Cox, 1745. First ed. Full contemporary calf. In this early novel Kirby, tutor to Edward Gibbon, tells the story of Automathes—a man able to survive for 19 years on a desolate island without any contact with human society. Jerry Beasley notes that *Automathes*, a "padded plagiarism of *The History of Autonous* (1736), combines Crusoesque desert-island adventure and utopian polemics" (p. 171). Block, p. 129; ESTC t93144.

Mather, Samuel. *An Abridgment of the Life of the Late Reverend and Learned Dr. Cotton Mather, of Boston in New-England.* London: Printed for J. Oswald & J. Brackstone, 1744. First ed. Full contemporary sheep (rebacked). In ink: "John Renals. 1804." This biography of Cotton Mather, a Puritan minister and the "last great member of a Puritan dynasty" (ANB), is abridged from a much longer account written by his son, Samuel Mather, in 1729. Also issued as part of a collection titled *Instructions to Ministers* (1744), this book aimed to serve as "a pattern to all Christians, who desire to excel in Holiness and Usefulness, and especially to younger ministers." ESTC t77813; Holmes 76-B.

Reynolds, Sir Joshua. *Seven Discourses Delivered in the Royal Academy by the President*. London: Printed for T. Cadell, 1778. First collected ed. Full contemporary tree calf. An English painter who specialized in portraits, Reynolds was also founder and first president of the Royal Academy of Arts. The publication of *Discourses*, polished lectures on art and painting, gave Reynolds a reputation as a man of letters. Samuel Johnson composed the Dedication to the King. Courtney, p. 129; ESTC t47974; Fleeman 78.5RD/1a; Hilles 11; NCBEL II 1176; Rothschild 1740.

Smollett, Tobias, translator. *The Adventures of Gil Blas of Santillane*. London: Printed for J. Osborn, 1750. Second ed., 4 vols. Full contemporary calf. In ink: "Tho. Ferrers." This picaresque novel, which describes "the knavery and foibles of life, with infinite humour and sagacity" (Brack & Chilton, p. xvii), was first published in French by Alain-René Lesage between 1715 and 1735 and translated into English by Smollett in 1749. In the preface to his first novel, *The Adventures of Roderick Random* (1748), Smollett acknowledges the influence of this tale on his own writing, deeming it the most successful of the "useful and entertaining" romances. Block, p. 137; ESTC t130653; NCBEL II 964; Raven 36; Tinker 1926; Wagoner 519.

Gothic Novels

Beckford, William. *An Arabian Tale, from an Unpublished Manuscript: With Notes Critical and Explanatory.* London: Printed for J. Johnson, 1786. First ed. Half contemporary calf over marbled boards (rebacked). In ink: "New College Oxford 1802." Written in French in 1782, Beckford's classic oriental novel *Vathek* was translated into English and published by scholar Samuel Henley in 1786. A masterpiece of bizarre invention and sustained fantasy, it relates the story of Caliph Vathek and his journey to Eblis, or hell. Lord Byron proclaimed that "this most Eastern and sublime tale surpasses all European imitations" (Cowan & Clark, p. 1). Block, p. 18; Chapman 3A; DNB; ESTC t62055; Garside et al. 1786: 15; NCBEL II 973; Rothschild 354; Summers, pp. 543–545.

Inchbald, Elizabeth. *A Simple Story.* London: Printed for G.G.J. & J. Robinson, 1791. First ed., 4 vols. Quarter contemporary calf over marbled boards. In ink: "L. Dickins." *A Simple Story* is the most memorable novel of this English novelist and actress. Its intriguing plot follows the love story of a young Miss Miller who falls for, and later marries, Dorriforth, a Catholic Priest. Maria Edgeworth wrote: "I have never read any novel that affected me so strongly, or that so completely possessed me with the belief in the real existence of all the people it represents" (Littlewood, p. 78). Block, p. 118; ESTC t134770; Garside et al. 1791: 41; Joughin, p. 68; NCBEL II 843; Summers, pp. 504–505.

Reeve, Clara. *The Two-Mentors: A Modern Story*. London: Printed for Charles Dilly, 1783. Second ed., 2 vols. Full contemporary calf. Reeve's innovative fiction inspired many of her fellow Gothic writers, including Horace Walpole and Mary Shelley. She classified novels as those "intended for amusement, and those further attempting to counteract the poison of fashion and folly" (Black, p. 53). This epistolary novel "contrasts the point of view of a licentious guardian with that of a virtuous tutor in their respectable letters to a sensible young hero" (Black, p. 5). Black 677; Block, p. 195; ESTC t118919; Garside et al. 1783: 19; NCBEL II 1007; Summers, p. 538.

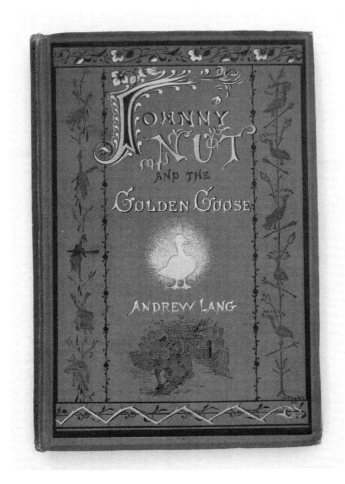

Cover of *Johnny Nut and the Golden Goose,* by
Andrew Lang (London: Longmans, Green, &
Co., 1887).

19TH-CENTURY BRITISH FICTION

The nineteenth century was Fales's favorite period, a time when "the novel really bloomed," according to Fales (New York University, *Bulletin*, Society for the Libraries, Winter 1959). It is no surprise that the Collection is strongest in British fiction from this era, particularly Victorian novels. The later nineteenth century is also when more books for children began to appear. Spurred by the rise of education and reading, children's literature from 1865 to 1899 was especially varied. This section also highlights Gothic novels from 1800 to 1820, continuing the list begun in the previous section.

Ainsworth, William Harrison. *Jack Sheppard: A Romance.* London: Richard Bentley, 1839. First ed., 3 vols. Green publisher's cloth. Binder's ticket of William George's Sons, Bristol. Ainsworth's tale, based on the real-life events of notorious thief Jack Sheppard, was so popular that "the huge sale of the book exceeded that of *Oliver Twist* [1839]" (Ellis, p. 358). Integral to the text's initial notoriety were the etchings done by George Cruikshank, a leading illustrator of the period. Thackeray felt that Cruikshank "really wrote the tale" and that Ainsworth, who Fales deemed "a charming and interesting writer of tales" (p. 6), "simply put words to it" (Buckley, p. 432). Block, p. 5; Cohn, *A Bibliographical Catalogue* 11; Cohn, *George Cruikshank* 1982–2002; Locke, pp. 9–10; NCBEL III 911; Sadleir 14; Wolff 53.

De la Ramée, Marie Louise. (Ouida.) *Signa. A Story.* London: Chapman & Hall, 1875. First ed., 3 vols. Blue publisher's cloth. In ink: "B.K." Circulating library label of W.H. Smith & Sons. Jack London claimed that "reading Ouida's *Signa* at eight years of age" was a primary factor in his literary success (Labor, p. 512). "The plot of *Signa* is melodramatic, but will not seem unrealistic to anyone moderately familiar with police-court news" (Stirling, p. 111). A favorite author of the circulating libraries, Ouida was perhaps the most popular novelist of the 1870s. DNB; NCBEL III 1070; Sadleir 1938a; Wolff 5343.

Dickens, Charles. *The Battle of Life. A Love Story.* London: Bradbury & Evans, 1846. First ed., fourth issue, Todd's state E1. Scarlet publisher's cloth. To say that Dickens was a favorite of Fales is an understatement; he was second only to Sir Walter Scott. This is the fourth of Dickens's five Christmas Books that appeared between 1843 and 1848, the first being *A Christmas Carol.* Staying in Switzerland, Dickens encountered great difficulty in writing this book; it was "his most flawed and disliked" (Schlicke, p. 34). Released to generally hostile reviews, *Battle of Life* still sold 23,000 copies on the first day of publication. Block, p. 59; Carr B417; Eckel, pp. 121–124; NCBEL III 811; Podeschi A116; Sadleir 681 (second issue); Tinker 826 (third issue).

Doyle, Arthur Conan. *The Refugees: A Tale of Two Continents*. London: Longmans, Green, & Co., 1893. First ed., 3 vols. Green publisher's cloth. Armorial bookplate of E. Hubert Litchfield; circulating library label of Cawthorn, Hutt & Son. In describing this work, Doyle, creator of detective Sherlock Holmes, wrote "I take a New Englander, a Puritan...and a New Yorker, the woodman...and I precipitate these two into the court of Louis XIV, and mix them up in the European history of that time" (Green & Gibson A12). According to the collector Robert Wolff (1912), this is a very rare book. NCBEL III 1046; Parke-Bernet Galleries 336.

Edgeworth, Maria. *Castle Rackrent; An Hibernian Tale. Taken from Facts, and From the Manners of the Irish Squires, Before the Year 1782*. London: Printed by Luke Hansard for J. Johnson, 1800. Second ed. Full contemporary tree calf. Referred to by Fales as the "smallest giant of her era" (p. 6), Edgeworth was a prolific Anglo-Irish novelist and educational writer and a significant figure in the Romantic movement. *Castle Rackrent*, arguably the most celebrated of Edgeworth's works, draws on her domestic experience and family background to record the fictional memoirs of "the Irish servant of a family of feckless Anglo-Irish gentry" (Todd, p. 110). Block, p. 65; ESTC t143397; Garside et al. 1800: 30 (first ed.); Loeber & Loeber E20; NCBEL III 666; Sadleir 763 (first ed.); Slade 5B; Wolff 1984.

Gore, Catherine. *The Snow Storm, A Christmas Story*. London and Paris: Fisher, Son, & Co., [1854?]. Third ed. Red publisher's cloth. Michael Sadleir (1034 first ed., p. 144) remarked that "no one, seeking to recreate the affectations, arrogance and pasteboard splendours of smart Society during the eighteen-thirties and forties, can afford to ignore [Gore's work]." These "silver-fork" novels, extolling the virtues of male domination and female submissiveness, were extremely popular. Featuring an etched frontispiece and three plates by George Cruikshank, this is the first of three Christmas Books—the others being *New Year's Day* (1846) and *The Inundation* (1847). Block, p. 88; Cohn, *A Bibliographical Catalogue* 342; Cohn, *George Cruikshank* 2376–2379; NCBEL III 727; Wolff 2639 (first ed.).

Hardy, Thomas. *Far from the Madding Crowd*. New York: Henry Holt & Co., 1874. First American ed. Cream publisher's cloth. In ink: "Clara M. Ward" and "Geo. Ward." Published as part of Holt's Leisure Hour series, the American edition of this work, Hardy's first major literary success, was published five days after the London edition. According to a review by Andrew Lang, this work is "so clever a novel, so original in atmosphere and in character, that its brilliant qualities are likely to neutralize the glare of its equally prominent faults" (*The Academy*, Jan. 2, 1875, p. 9). NCBEL III 981; Purdy, p. 17.

Le Fanu, Joseph Sheridan. *A Lost Name*. London: Richard
Bentley, 1868. First ed., 3 vols. Sand publisher's cloth.
An Irish novelist and newspaper proprietor, Le Fanu
was central to the development of the ghost story in the
Victorian era. This, a suspense novel, was first serialized in London's *Temple Bar* from May 1867 to May
1868. It "concerns the struggle of Mark Shadwell, the
owner of Raby Hall, against despair after murdering
his first cousin" (Loeber & Loeber L112). Shadwell,
who commits suicide at the end of the tale, also has an
affair with his daughter's French governess. NCBEL III
942; Sadleir 1381; Wolff 4018.

Scott, Sir Walter. *Tales of My Landlord, Fourth and Last Series, Collected and Arranged by Jedidiah Cleishbotham*.
Edinburgh: Printed for Robert Cadell; London: Whit-
taker & Co., 1832. First ed., 4 vols. Publisher's drab
paper boards (rebacked). Scott, the most successful author of his day (and Fales's favorite to collect),
published his final two novels—*Castle Dangerous*, set
during the Wars of Scottish Independence, and *Count
Robert of Paris*, set during the First Crusade—together
as the final set in his Tales of My Landlord series. As
Scott admitted, the title is misleading, for the tales were
not told by any fictional landlord. Block, p. 210; DNB;
NCBEL III 674; Todd & Bowden 253A; Worthington 23.

Thackeray, William Makepeace. *A Shabby Genteel Story, and Other Tales*. New York: D. Appleton & Co., 1852. First ed. Red publisher's cloth. In ink: "J.W. Ladd. May 12 1899." Thackeray, best remembered today for his novel *Vanity Fair* (1847–48), was one of the most popular authors of the Victorian era. *A Shabby Genteel Story* is an early and unfinished novel; only the first part was completed. In discussing why the work was never finished, Thackeray noted, "The colors are long since dry; the artist's hand is changed. It is best to leave the sketch as it was when first designed" (Van Duzer 196). Brussel, p. 138; NCBEL III 857.

Trollope, Anthony. *The Last Chronicle of Barset*. London: Smith, Elder & Co., 1867. First ed., 2 vols. Half contemporary calf over marbled boards. Bookseller's ticket of T. Chapman Brown & Co., Leicester. The last of the six Barsetshire novels "worthily crowns the series in adding to it a new dimension through the dominating presence of the Revd. Mr. Crawley," a largely tragic figure (DNB). Writing in *The Spectator*, R.H. Hutton concluded, "Of its own light kind there has been no better novel ever written than *The Last Chronicle of Barset*" (DNB). Trollope himself agreed; he thought this was his best novel. Brussel, p. 153; NCBEL III 883; Sadleir, *Trollope* 26; Tinker 2206 (second ed.); Wolff 6784.

Gothic Novels

Burney, Sarah Harriet. *Traits of Nature*. London: Printed for Henry Colburn, 1813. Third ed., 5 vols. Half contemporary calf over marbled boards. The half-sister of novelist Fanny Burney, Sarah published her first novel, *Clarentine*, anonymously in 1796. In 1812, *Traits of Nature*, the first novel published under her own name, quickly sold out. A second edition was required three months later and a third in 1813. It is a "lively work in which lovers are caught between hostile families and the heroine seeks the approval of a tyrannical father" (DNB). Block, p. 30; Garside et al. 1812: 24 (first ed.); Summers, p. 536.

Maturin, Charles Robert. *Women: or, Pour et Contre*. Edinburgh: Printed by James Ballantyne and Co. for Archibald Constable & Co.; London: Longman, Hurst, Rees, Orme, & Brown, 1818. First ed., 3 vols. Half contemporary calf over marbled boards. An early example of the psychological novel, *Women* is set in the author's native Dublin. Maturin, someone who "wrote melodramas that blazed with incest and malice and violence" (Wilt, p. 257), brought unprecedented violence and cruelty to the Gothic form. Block, p. 156; Garside et al. 1818: 41; Loeber & Loeber M315; NCBEL III 746; Sadleir 1670; Summers, pp. 562–563; Wolff 4653.

Owenson, Sydney, Lady Morgan. *Woman: or, Ida of Athens*. London: Printed for Longman, Hurst, Rees, & Orme, 1809. First ed., 4 vols. Full contemporary polished calf (rebacked). A heavily-researched epistolary novel set in a remote part of Connacht, Ireland, *Woman* earned Owenson £700. In a review, Jane Austen remarked, "her Irish Girl does not make me expect much. If the warmth of her language could afford the Body it might be worth reading in this weather" (Stevenson, p. 116). Block, p. 167; Garside et al. 1809: 55; Loeber & Loeber M552; NCBEL III 754; Sadleir 1785; Summers, p. 561.

Porter, Jane. *The Pastor's Fire-Side, A Novel*. London: Printed for Longman, Hurst, Rees, Orme, & Brown, 1817. First ed., 4 vols. Half contemporary sheep over marbled boards (rebacked). Porter, best known during her lifetime for *The Scottish Chiefs* (1810), believed that her historical novels influenced the writing of Sir Walter Scott. This novel "shows a more than usually acute since of local colour in its delineation of the area round Lindisfarne" (DNB) and ends, as a review notes, "with the hero's return to England, and marriage with a Spanish lady" (*British Lady's Magazine and Monthly Miscellany*, Mar. 1817, pp. 165–169). Block, p. 188; Garside et al. 1817: 49; NCBEL III 758; Summers, p. 458; Wolff 5606.

Children's Literature

Dodgson, Charles. (Lewis Carroll.) *Sylvie and Bruno.* London and New York: Macmillan & Co., 1889. First ed. Red publisher's cloth. In ink: "1915." Carroll, the author of *Alice in Wonderland* (1865) and a lecturer in mathematics at Oxford University, penned *Sylvie and Bruno* and its sequel *Sylvie and Bruno Concluded* (1893) later in his life. Both were illustrated by Harry Furniss. Containing two main plots—one set in Victorian England and the other in the world of Fairyland—*Sylvie and Bruno* is full of the "ideals and sentiments" Carroll held dear, although it also contains a "good deal of nonsense" (Kunitz & Haycraft, p. 120). NCBEL III 978; Parrish, *Lewis Carroll*, p. 36; Williams 56.

Jefferies, Richard. *Bevis: The Story of a Boy.* London: Sampson Low, Marston, Searle, & Rivington, 1882. First ed., 3 vols. Brown publisher's cloth. Advertisements dated December 1881. Jefferies, writer and mystic, was noted for his sketches of natural history and rural life. Some claim that *Bevis*, based on Jefferies' childhood in rural England, is "the best boys' book ever written" (DNB). The title character, who first appeared in *Wood Magic* (1881), is here celebrated for having "visionary moments" on adventures with his friend Mark at "New Sea." Miller & Matthews B15.1 (binding B); NCBEL III 1061; Sadleir 1305; Wolff 3615.

Lang, Andrew. *Johnny Nut and the Golden Goose*. London: Longmans, Green, & Co., 1887. First ed. Blue-green publisher's cloth. An important figure in the history of children's literature, Lang is best-remembered for his 25 "colored" fairy books: compilations of folk-tales from many parts of the world, beginning with *The Blue Fairy Book* in 1891. (The Fales Collection includes two of the 25.) In translating *Johnny Nut* from the French of folklorist Charles Deulin, Lang "sophisticates his original still more" (Green, pp. 84, 243). The moral of the story is that, above all else "we should be easily amused." DNB; NCBEL III 1441.

Stevenson, Robert Louis. *Kidnapped, Being Memoirs of the Adventures of David Balfour in the Year 1751*. [London]: Cassell & Co., Limited, 1886. First ed., first issue. Reddish-brown publisher's cloth (rebacked). Bookplate of John C. Eckel. First serialized in *Young Folks' Paper*, *Kidnapped* is far more than, in the words of Stevenson, "a book for the winter evening school-room when the tasks are over and the hour for bed draws near." With a fold-out map charting the course of protagonist David Balfour, it evokes the atmosphere of Scotland after the 1745 Jacobite rising. Its sequel, *Catriona* (1893), is also in the Fales Collection. Beinecke 378; DNB; NCBEL III 1006; Prideaux 18; Princeton University Library 31.

Yonge, Charlotte. *The Chaplet of Pearls; or, The White and Black Ribaumont*. London: Macmillan & Co., 1868. First ed., 2 vols. Green publisher's cloth. In ink: "R. Harvey." Influenced greatly by Oxford Movement Anglicanism, Yonge was able to keep several projects running concurrently. She wrote over 200 works of fiction and nonfiction, in addition to articles for her own magazine, *The Monthly Packet*. In this historical novel, Yonge "makes young Berenger, bred up in the England of the second half of the sixteenth century, find himself more at home at the Mass than in a Huguenot conventicle" (Battiscombe, p. 132). NCBEL III 973; Wolff IV, p. 289.

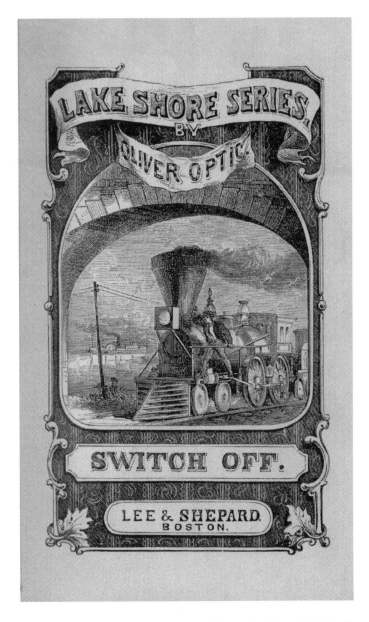

Added engraved title page to William T. Adams's *Switch
Off; or, The War of The Students* (Boston: Lee & Shepard,
1870).

19TH-CENTURY AMERICAN FICTION

American literature, with distinctively American characteristics, came into its own in the nineteenth century. Fales was very interested in the American novels of this formative era, collecting the works of nearly every early canonical author as well as lesser-known works that document the changing landscapes, literary and otherwise, of the United States. Here I have highlighted regional tales—stories that describe nineteenth-century life in the Creole South, the Far West, coastal New England, metropolitan New York, and the prairies of Middle America.

Adams, William T. (Oliver Optic.) *Switch Off; or, The War of The Students.* Boston: Lee & Shepard, 1870. First ed., second issue. Green publisher's cloth. In ink: "Coldric B. Silliman, A Christmas Present, 1870." This novel is one of Oliver Optic's Lake Shore series of Civil War-inspired adventure novels. According to the preface, the principle events of *Switch Off* involve "the students of Toppleton Institute, among whom the war indicated on the title page occurred." With more than 120 novels and 1,000 articles and short stories, Adams was one of the highest-paid writers in late nineteenth-century America, and his books sold more than two million copies. ANB; Jones, *"Oliver Optic" Checklist* 70 (first issue).

Alcott, Louisa May. *Little Women or, Meg, Jo, Beth, and Amy Part Second*. Boston: Roberts Brothers, 1869. First ed., second state. Green publisher's cloth (rebacked). When Alcott's publisher asked her to write a "girls' book," she accepted the offer only because she needed the money. The result was one of the best-selling novels of all time. Part one, issued in 1868, did not sell at first. This book, part second, was also issued in a small edition, "but it went like wildfire, and pulled part one along with it" (Grolier American 74). Within four years, this classic American story of girls growing up sold 82,000 copies. American Firsts, p. 13; ANB; BAL 159; Gulliver, pp. 28–30; High Spots, p. 12; Parley to Penrod, p. 30.

Arthur, Timothy Shay. *Ten Nights in a Bar-Room, and What I Saw There*. Boston: L.P. Crown & Co.; Philadelphia: J.W. Bradley, 1854. First ed. Brown publisher's cloth, with two wood engravings by Van Ingen. In ink: "Elliot Aug. 8th, 1861." This bestseller, which rivaled *Uncle Tom's Cabin* (1852) in popularity, helped demonize alcohol in the eyes of the American public. "Every Sunday School library had to have it, it satisfied the appetite for the sensational and lurid and at the same time was endorsed by the clergy and was the one book of fiction which young America might safely read on Sunday" (Grolier American 62). Wright, *1851–1875* 131.

Chesnutt, Charles. *The Wife of His Youth, and Other Stories of the Color Line*. Boston and New York: Houghton Mifflin & Company, 1899. First ed. Red publisher's cloth. In ink: "Dr. Geo. W. Potts, Asbury Park, N.J." Chesnutt was the first important African-American writer whose primary genre was fiction, and the first to be published primarily by the major publishing houses. In this collection, Chesnutt reveals the complex difficulties facing those who, like himself, aspired to rise in society despite their mixed race. American Firsts, p. 106; ANB; Whiteman, p. 15; Wright, *1876–1900* 1019.

Clemens, Samuel Langhorne (Mark Twain.) *Merry Tales.* New York: Charles L. Webster & Co., 1892. First ed. Grey-green publisher's cloth. Presentation copy: "With the compliments of the editor, March 1892." Part of Webster's Fiction, Fact, and Fancy Series, this collection of seven short stories is described in the Editor's Note as ranking with "the better class of native literature" now available at "moderate prices." Even at bargain rates (75¢ each) the collection sold poorly and contributed to Twain's eventual financial collapse. Twain himself referred to it as "the mess" (Robinson, pp. 2–3). American Firsts, p. 111; BAL 3435 (binding A); Johnson, *Mark Twain*, pp. 64–65; Wright, *1876–1900* 1094.

Cooper, James Fenimore. *The Red Rover, A Tale*. Philadelphia: Carey, Lea & Carey, 1828. First American ed., 2 vols. Volume 1 rebound in red buckram, volume 2 in publisher's blue-grey paper boards (rebacked). Cooper is generally considered the creator of the genre known as sea fiction—a genre that Fales, a navy veteran, was fascinated with. This seafaring tale follows the activities of sailor Dick Fid, free black sailor Scipio Africans, and Royal Navy officer James Wilder as they encounter the infamous pirate The Red Rover. American Firsts, p. 123; ANB; BAL 3839; Brussel, p. 7; Spiller & Blackburn, 7; Wright, *1774–1850* 703.

Crawford, Francis Marion. *Katharine Lauderdale*. London and New York: Macmillan & Co., 1894. First English ed., 3 vols. Blue publisher's cloth. Circulating library label of Mudie's Select Library. By 1896, books by Crawford had sold more than 600,000 copies in America, making him "one of the most popular novelists of the eighties and nineties" (Wolff I, p. 301, 1561). In this picture of the "money and jealously" contained within the Lauderdales and other upper-class New York families (Wolff I, p. 304), Crawford reveals an undercurrent of "strife and intrigue, of love and jealousy and hatred" (*Harrisburg Telegraph*, Apr. 16, 1894, p. 2). One of the last Victorian three-deckers published, this copy was originally owned by Charles Mudie's circulating library. ANB; BAL 4180; Sadleir 642.

Harte, Bret. *A Millionaire of Rough-and-Ready and Devil's Ford*. Boston and New York: Houghton, Mifflin Company, 1887. First ed. Brown publisher's cloth. In ink: "Anna W. Bunting Feb. 1887." Cut-out portrait and facsimile signature of Harte pasted in. Born in Albany, New York, Harte was known for "the colorful miners, gamblers, pioneers, and other Western characters which he so brilliantly depicted" (Grolier American, pp. 107–108). Written in Harte's "familiar vein" and featuring "rough and ignorant miners who strike gold" and "their beautiful daughters and wives" these two "spirited and well told" stories depict California in its early days (PW, Feb. 12, 1887, p. 7). American Firsts, p. 217; ANB; BAL 7339 (binding A); Scharnhorst 904; Wright, *1876–1900* 2544.

Hawthorne, Nathaniel. *The Snow-Image, and Other Twice-Told Tales*. Boston: Ticknor, Reed, & Fields, 1852. First ed. Brown publisher's cloth. Book-label of Walter P. Chrysler, Jr. The author of *The Scarlet Letter* (1850), Hawthorne was one of the most significant writers of the antebellum period. He completed this work, his last collection of short fiction, while living in Lenox, Massachusetts. It includes the first appearance in book form of his much-anthologized tale "My Kinsman, Major Molineux," about America on the verge of revolution. American Firsts, p. 223; ANB; BAL 7607; Clark A19.1a; Wright, *1851–1875* 1140.

Melville, Herman. *The Refugee*. Philadelphia: T.B. Peterson & Brothers, 1865. First ed. thus. Red publisher's cloth. First published under the title *Israel Potter* in 1855 by G.P. Putnam, the plates of this work were legally sold to T.B. Peterson during the panic of 1857. Peterson reprinted the tale as *The Refugee*. Melville, outraged by the title change, remarked that "I have never written any work by that title." (This assertion appears in an undated clipping from the *New York World* inserted in a copy at the New York Public Library; see Minnigerode, p. 167.) Melville's personal objections resulted in the book's immediate withdrawal and in Merle Johnson's claim that *The Refugee* was a "pirated edition" (American Firsts, p. 355). It is not. BAL 13724; Cahoon, p. 16; Wright, *1851–1875* 1700.

Poe, Edgar Allan. *The Gold Bug*. Garden City, New York: Doubleday, Doran & Co., 1929. First ed. thus, trade issue. Yellow publisher's cloth. In ink: "J.L.H. Allen." First published in Philadelphia's *The Dollar Newspaper* in 1843, *The Gold Bug*, an early form of detective fiction, follows the life of William Legrand after he is bitten by a gold-colored bug. It was Poe's most widely read short story during his lifetime. Edited by Poe scholar Thomas Ollive Mabbott, this, the first critical edition, presents "the *complete* text of *The Gold Bug* containing all of Poe's major and minor alterations and additions." A limited issue of 377 copies was released in 1928. ANB; BAL 16186 (limited issue).

Westcott, Edward. *David Harum: A Story of American Life*. New York: D. Appleton & Co., 1898. First ed. Yellow publisher's cloth. In ink: "Mary Marymard December 25, 1898." This novel, about the "wit and wisdom of the kindly horse trader" (High Spots, p. 76) in the fictitious upstate New York town of Homeville, sold more than 400,000 copies within its first two years. As one reviewer noted, "David Harum is an old county banker, quaint, dry, and somewhat illiterate, whose odd philosophy and queer stories have delighted many readers" (PW, Jan. 28, 1899, p. 102). American Firsts, p. 516; ANB; BAL 21313; Wright, *1876–1900* 5876.

Whitman, Walt. *Franklin Evans; or The Inebriate. A Tale of the Times*. New York: Random House, 1929. First ed. thus. Blue marbled-patterned publisher's cloth. Whitman's first book and his only novel, *Franklin Evans* was first issued in 1842 as a supplement to *The New World*, a monthly newspaper. A temperance novel, the work is centered around the rags-to-riches story of its protagonist, Franklin Evans. Years later Whitman, who also penned *Leaves of Grass* (1855), claimed he was embarrassed by the book and called it "damned rot" (Castiglia & Hendler, p. xxi). American Firsts, p. 528 (first ed.); BAL 21393 (first ed.); Oscar Lion Collection, p. 26.

Whittier, John Greenleaf, & Lucy Larcom. *Child Life in Prose*. Boston: James R. Osgood & Company, 1874. Green publisher's cloth. Presentation copy: "Edmund S. Spalding. With the love of Lucy Larcom, Christmas 1873." Edited and with contributions by New England poets Whittier and Larcom, this work is "an anthology of fine sayings and doings of the little ones" (*New York Herald*, Aug. 8, 1873, p. 2). "It is not intended exclusively for children, but for all who appreciate the beauty and charm of healthy child-life" (*Commercial Advertiser*, Oct. 25, 1873, p. 2). American Firsts, p. 539; BAL 11334, 21915; Currier, pp. 121–122.

Woolson, Constance Fenimore. *Jupiter Lights: A Novel*. New York: Harper & Brothers, 1889. First ed. Brown publisher's cloth. In pencil: "DeC Fales." First published in *Harper's Magazine*, this book by the niece of J.F. Cooper takes its title from two lighthouses bearing the name of Jupiter Light—one near Savannah, Georgia, and the other on the southern shore of Lake Superior. Regarded by the *Newark Advertiser* as "one of the strongest works which the field of American fiction has produced in many years" (PW, June 28, 1890, p. 838) it features two women, "both of whom love an abusive ne'er-do-well, Ferdinand Morrison" (ANB). BAL 23468; Wright, *1876–1900* 6106.

Regional Fiction

Cable, George Washington. *"Posson Jone'" and Père Raphaël with A Word Setting Forth How and Why the Two Tales are One.* New York: Charles Scribner's Sons, 1909. First ed. thus. Blue-gray publisher's cloth. After the publication of *Old Creole Days* (1879), a collection of stories presenting the history of New Orleans in which "Posson Jone'" first appeared, Cable "came to be perceived not simply as a regional writer, but as one of the most important authors in the United States" (ANB). In his Introduction, Cable claims that these accounts of Creole life, told from two points of view, are "a genuine love-match, made in heaven, as lovers say, and bred of an affinity back of all time!" American Firsts, p. 93; BAL 2377.

Irving, Washington. *A Tour on the Prairies.* Philadelphia: Carey, Lea, & Blanchard, 1835. First American ed., first state. Green publisher's muslin. Irving, author of "The Legend of Sleepy Hollow" (1820), was arguably the most important American author of the early nineteenth century. In 1832 he traveled "to the country west of the Mississippi" with U.S. Commissioner of Indian Tribes Henry Ellsworth. Published as the first volume of the three-volume Crayon Miscellany, this portrait of the "original West" is a romanticized account of that journey. American Firsts, p. 277; BAL 10140 (label and catalog A); Brussel, p. 56; Bryant, p. 32; Langfield, p. 33; Wright, *1774–1850* 1401.

Jewett, Sarah Orne. *Betty Leicester: A Story for Girls*. Boston and New York: Houghton Mifflin & Co., 1890. First ed., later (but prior to the sixth) printing. Red and white publisher's cloth. In ink: "Mary Higginson from Dada. December 25th, 1889." Jewett's heroine is a 15-year-old girl who spends a summer in a quiet seaside village while her father is away. The novel introduces "those quaint types of New England character, especially of the seafaring kind, in which Miss Jewett delights" (*Boston Journal*, Nov. 19, 1889, suppl. 1, p. 1). The book's cover was designed by the artist Sarah Wyman Whitman. American Firsts, p. 294; BAL 10895; Parley to Penrod, p. 93; Weber & Weber, p. 13.

Lippard, George. *The Empire City; or, New York by Night and Day*. Philadelphia: T.B. Peterson & Brothers, 1864. Second ed. Rebound in blue buckram. The social reformer Lippard "dramatized social injustice and upper-class corruption in America's rapidly expanding cities" (ANB). The second of four "urban exposé novels," this 1864 edition claims to be "the most absorbing novel of the age." "Come with me, then, and let us look upon—*The Empire City*—into whose streets and homes and temples, flows the virtue and the crime, the luxury and the misery, of the Old World and the New." ANB; BAL 11807; Jackson, *George Lippard*, pp. 153–154; Wright, *1774–1850* 1681 (first ed.).

White, William Allen. *The Court of Boyville*. New York: Doubleday & McClure Co., 1899. Tan publisher's cloth. First ed. White's reputation as a shrewd spokesman for the values of Middle America prompted H.L. Mencken to dub him the "Sage of Emporia." Displaying a "taste for sentiment and nostalgia for childhood" (ANB), these six short stories chronicle the escapades of "Piggy" Pennington and his friends. The *Wichita Eagle* noted, "The virtue of White's stories is that they dwarf you instantly to the boy's size and enlarge your soul to the boundless dimensions of a boy's soul" (PW, Dec. 2, 1899, p. 1205). American Firsts, p. 526; Parley to Penrod, p. 109.

Illustration by Aubrey Beardsley, facing page 82 of *The Poems of Ernest Dowson* (London and New York: John Lane, The Bodley Head, 1905).

POETRY AND VERSE

Fales was especially interested in poets who also wrote prose, and in those whose works were especially representative of their times. Highlighted in this section are four of the five Fireside Poets—New England poets who, in the nineteenth century, had "a popular readership, a cultural power, and a presence in public life that later poets could only dream of" (Bendixen & Burt, p. 260). (The fifth Fireside Poet, William Cullen Bryant, is represented in the Nonfiction—Biography section.) The term "Fireside" comes from the fact that their poetry was read around household fires, often aloud to a gathered family.

Aiken, Conrad. *The Kid.* New York: Duell, Sloan & Pearce, 1947. First ed. Light-brown publisher's cloth. Aiken received the most prestigious of literary awards, including a Pulitzer Prize and a National Book Award, along with the critical acclaim of the most respected writers and critics of his generation. He never became a truly popular poet, however. In this narrative poem, William Blackstone, a seventeenth-century European who owned much of what is now Boston, is taken as a "symbol of the American search for individual liberty" (PW, Sept. 27, 1947, p. 1715). ANB; Bonnell A37.

Allston, Washington. *The Sylphs of the Seasons, with Other Poems*. Boston: Cummings & Hilliard, 1813. First American ed. Rebound in brown buckram. In ink: "Sarah Moore." After graduating from Harvard as class poet in 1800, Allston departed for England to study painting under Benjamin West at London's Royal Academy. Allston's interest in poetry was renewed when he met Coleridge in Rome. "The Sylphs of the Season," which lent its title to this, his first collection, employs the Scottish stanza. His couplets, as in "Two Painters," "ring of the age of Pope in their wit" (Bendixen & Burt, p. 164). BAL 494 (thin-paper ed.); DNB.

Brooke, Rupert. *Poems*. London: Sidgwick & Jackson, 1911. First ed. Blue publisher's cloth with paper spine label. Brooke, a key poet of the First World War, died of blood poisoning in the Aegean Sea the day before his battalion landed for the bloody battle at Gallipoli in 1915. This, one of 500 copies printed, is Brooke's first collection of poetry; it was published when the poet was just 23. Dismissed by some critics as "patriotic gush," Brooke's poetry appears "surprisingly fresh, sometimes funny, playful, and attractively odd" (Phillips et al., p. 122). Keynes, *Rupert Brooke* 5; NCBEL IV 241.

Burns, Robert. *Poems*. Edinburgh: Printed for James Morison by John Moir, 1811. First ed. thus, 2 vols. Full contemporary calf (rebacked). Armorial bookplate of Admiral & Mrs. Benjamin Page. These volumes, owned and annotated by four generations of the Page family, were clearly a cherished set. With an account of Burns's life by Josiah Walker, this edition was the first to contain "Epitaph on a Country Laird." Hailed as the national poet of Scotland, Burns has enjoyed "almost unprecedented vitality and popularity" (Phillips et al., p. 30). Egerer, *A Bibliography*, p. 131; NCBEL III 1981.

Dowson, Ernest. *The Poems of Ernest Dowson*. London & New York: John Lane, The Bodley Head, 1905. First ed. Green publisher's cloth. A contributor to such magazines as *The Yellow Book* and *The Savoy*, Dowson was "imbued with [the spirit of the Nineties] to the point of saturation" (May, p. 115). This collected volume of poetry, with an introductory memoir by author Arthur Symons, is a product of the fin de siècle. Referring to Aubrey Beardsley's design for the cover, James Lewis May writes, "If Beardsley sums up the decade which we call the Nineties, that design itself sums up Beardsley" (May, p. 44). NCBEL III 624; Samuels Lasner 146.

Eliot, T.S. *Journey of the Magi*. London: Faber & Gwyer, 1927. First ed., limited issue. Yellow paper wrappers. Signed by the author: "T.S. Eliot." After Eliot's conversion to the Church of England in 1927, his poetry became increasingly religious. This is the first of five poems that Eliot contributed to The Ariel Poems, a series of 38 pamphlets that contain illustrated poems by various authors. Seventeen are in the Fales Collection. Eliot's Ariel poems "mediate on spiritual growth and anticipate the dialogue of self and soul" that is achieved in the much longer *Ash-Wednesday* (1930) (ANB). Gallup A9b; NCBEL IV 160.

Frost, Robert. *A Witness Tree*. New York: Henry Holt & Co., 1942. First trade ed. Blue publisher's cloth. Frost was awarded the 1943 Pulitzer Prize for Poetry (his fourth) for this collection of poems, which includes some of his finest works such as "The Most of It" and "The Silken Tent." However, the volume is perhaps most notable for "The Gift Outright," which was recited by John F. Kennedy at his 1961 presidential inauguration. Frost's publishers advertised that this volume "will substantiate still further his claim to permanence and importance." ANB; Crane A25.1.

Kipling, Rudyard. *Barrack Room Ballads and Other Verses.* London: Methuen & Co., 1892. First English ed. Red publisher's cloth (rebacked). Bookplate of John Langhorne. The first English-language writer to receive the Nobel Prize in Literature, Kipling was an accomplished poet. Holbrook Jackson remarked that when this collection of soldier songs, including "Mandalay," was released, "it was as though a bombshell had burst among the seats of literary judgement.... Academic criticism was faced with the necessity of revising its idea of poetry, and ultimately of making room for a new poet" (p. 232). Livingston, *Kipling* 90; NCBEL III 1022; Richards A69; Stewart 108.

Lewis, Matthew Gregory, ed. *Tales of Wonder.* London: Printed by W. Bulmer and Co. for the author; and sold by J. Bell, 1801. First ed., 2 vols. Bound together in contemporary mottled calf (rebacked). Nicknamed *Tales of Plunder* because of its "fine format and high price" (Summers, p. 529), *Tales of Wonder* contains well-known Gothic ballads and poems collected by M.G. "Monk" Lewis. This collection, which was mercilessly criticized and parodied, also contains contributions by Robert Southey, later Poet Laurate, and some of the earliest published poetry of Sir Walter Scott. NCBEL III 743; Peck, p. 275; Tinker 1496; Todd & Bowden 7Aa.

Masters, Edgar Lee. *Spoon River Anthology*. New York: The Macmillan Company, 1915. First ed., first issue. Blue-green publisher's cloth. Bookseller's ticket of Brentano's, New York. Ezra Pound began his review of these free verse characterizations that "capture small-town America, Midwest values, and the angst of modern life" by proclaiming that "at last, America has discovered a poet" (ANB). Selling 80,000 copies within a few short years, it became "that rarest of things, a poetry best seller" (Bendixen & Burt, p. 509). American Firsts, p. 352; ANB; High Spots, p. 56.

Percy, Thomas. *Reliques of Ancient English Poetry*. London: Printed for J. Dodsley, 1765. First ed., 3 vols. Full contemporary calf. In ink: "A. Rigby." Deemed "An epoch making book in the history of English literature" (dealer's description in NYU copy), this collection of ballads and popular songs greatly influenced British Romanticism. Wordsworth, who exclaimed that "poetry has been absolutely redeemed by it" (DNB), was inspired to write his own ballads in imitation (*Lyrical Ballads*, 1798, with Coleridge). The dedication, though signed by Percy, "owed its finest strokes to the superior pen of Dr. Johnson" (Courtney, p. 111). DNB; ESTC t84936; Fleeman 65.2PR/1; Grolier English 45; NCBEL II 243; Tinker 1662.

Robinson, Edwin Arlington. *Modred; A Fragment*. New York, New Haven, Princeton: Edmond Byrne Hackett: Brick Row Bookshop, 1929. First authorized ed. Publisher's blue paper-covered boards. The first major American poet of the twentieth century, Robinson was "unique in that he devoted his life to poetry and willingly paid the price in poverty and obscurity" (ANB). Here, published in a fine press edition of 250 copies signed by Robinson, is a "deleted fragment" from "Lancelot" (1920), the second of his three long, Arthurian-related poems (Hogan, p. 35). *Modred* first appeared a year earlier in the pirated *Three Poems* (1928). According to legend, Modred was made a Knight of the Round Table by King Arthur. American Firsts, p. 439.

Sassoon, Siegfried. *The Old Huntsman and Other Poems*. London: William Heinemann, 1917. First ed., first impression. Publisher's drab paper boards (rebacked). With the errata slip. This, Sassoon's first regularly published work of poetry, brings together a number of poems—written "under the shadow of war" and first published in *The Cambridge Magazine*—along with others previously found only in privately issued pamphlets (Keynes, *Siegfried Sassoon* A15a). Geoffrey Keynes has noted that "Sassoon's high reputation as one of the 'war poets,' facing the realities of war and inspired by pity and indignation, was established by this volume" (p. 10). NCBEL IV 338.

Tennyson, Alfred. *Enoch Arden, etc.* London: Edward Moxon & Co., 1864. First ed. Green publisher's cloth. Published during Tennyson's tenure as Poet Laureate, *Enoch Arden* is a narrative poem about a fisherman turned merchant sailor. A few copies were issued with the title *Idylls of the Hearth*, but, at the last moment, "after the sheets of the book had been printed off, the Poet decided to drop the general title *Idylls of the Hearth*, and to substitute for it the simpler one *Enoch Arden, etc.* .... Evidently the Poet was uncertain as to his title from the first" (Wise, *Tennyson* 107). Livingston, *Tennyson*, p. 49; NCBEL III 415; Tinker 2083.

Whitman, Sarah Helen. *Hours of Life, and Other Poems.* Providence: George H. Whitney, 1853. First ed. Brown publisher's cloth. In ink: "Vernon Lee Norwood." Many of the poems in this volume, Whitman's first collection of verse, "are gentle and sincere but unoriginal in content and style and not very darling" (ANB). Although she was a talented lyricist, Whitman is most remembered today for her relationship with Edgar Allan Poe, who twice proposed marriage. Claiming the title of "Poe's Helen," Whitman rejected Poe both times, the latter because her mother, who controlled the family finances, disapproved of the union. BAL 21366 (binding A).

Wordsworth, William. *The Recluse*. London and New York: Macmillan & Co., 1888. First ed., first printing. Green publisher's cloth. Along with Coleridge, Wordsworth helped to launch British Romanticism. *The Recluse*, according to Thomas Wise, "though in a way complete in itself, does not constitute a completed work." Beginning in 1798, "Wordsworth had planned a long and elaborate autographical poem to consist of three Parts and a Prelude, to bear the title *The Recluse*," but all the poet lived to produce were *The Prelude* (1850), *The Excursion* (1814), and the present poem "Home at Grasmere," which was left in manuscript at his death and "which represents the first Part of the first Book only." (All quotations are from Wise, *Wordsworth* 34.) DNB; Healey 251; NCBEL III 187; Reed A212; Tinker 2359; Wise, *Two Lake Poets*, p. 36.

Yeats, William Butler. *The Countess Kathleen and Various Legends and Lyrics*. London: T. Fisher Unwin, 1892. First ed. (Cameo Series). Green paper boards with parchment spine. This, Yeats's second collection, contains the first appearance in book form of "The Lake Isle of Innisfree" and "When You Are Old." With the publication of this work and *Celtic Twilight* (1893, also in the Fales Collection), Yeats's "new voice was hailed as something more than new; it was hailed as a strong and persuasive voice that was already attracting to itself affinities in the land of its origin" (Jackson, *The Eighteen Nineties*, pp. 149). NCBEL III 1918; Wade 6.

The Fireside Poets

Holmes, Oliver Wendell, John O. Sargent, & Park Benjamin. *The Harbinger; A May Gift.* Boston: Carter, Hendee, & Co., 1833. First ed. Blue publisher's muslin (rebacked). Bookplate of Carroll Atwood Wilson. In ink: "Mary Appleton Oct. 18. 1833." This volume contains 17 poems by Holmes, 17 by Sargent, and 19 by Benjamin. Printed for the benefit of the New England Institution for the Blind and sold at their May Fair in 1833, it was the first appearance in book form of 13 of Holmes's poems, including "The Ballad of the Oysterman." The Institution raised $500 through the sale of the book. American Firsts, p. 253; BAL 977, 8723; Currier & Tilton, pp. 22–23; Tinker 1226; Wilson & Randall, p. 471.

Longfellow, Henry Wadsworth. *The Song of Hiawatha.* Boston: Ticknor & Fields, 1855. First American ed., first printing and without the "n" on page 279. Brown publisher's cloth. Described by the poet as an "Indian Edda," this work, which embodies the traditional stories, legends, and poetry of the Native Americans living near Lake Superior, was inspired by the Finnish epic *Kalevala. The Song of Hiawatha* has been called "the most popular poem in American literary history" (Bendixen & Burt, p. 256). American Firsts, p. 325; ANB; BAL 12112; Brussel, p. 92; Grolier American 66; High Spots, p. 53; Livingston, *Longfellow*, p. 57.

Lowell, James Russell. *Melibœus-Hipponax. The Biglow Papers*. Cambridge: Published by George Nichols, 1848. First ed., first issue. Light-brown publisher's cloth (rebacked). Lowell's humor is best revealed in this "curious little masterpiece" of political satire in verse (ANB). The *Papers* employ, to brilliant effect, the first-person vernacular of a fictional Yankee farmer, Hosea Biglow. Fueled by Lowell's view that America's war with Mexico was "of false pretenses," *The Biglow Papers* is considered "the finest political satire of nineteenth-century America" (ANB). American Firsts, p. 332; BAL 13068 (binding A); Bendixen & Burt, p. 275; Grolier American 57; Grolier English 86; High Spots, p. 54; Livingston, *Lowell*, p. 33.

Whittier, John Greenleaf. *The Tent on the Beach, and Other Poems*. Boston: Ticknor & Fields, 1867. First ed., BAL's mixed state; Currier's third impression. Green publisher's cloth. In pencil: "May 1867." Afraid that the poem was too full of "self-praise and egotism" (Currier, pp. 101–105), Whittier twice rewrote several of the stanzas on pages 45 and 46 while the book was still in press. Therefore, each impression features a slightly different version of the poem. This, the third impression, contains an intermediate version. Our copy was thoroughly annotated by an early owner. American Firsts, p. 535; BAL 21866 (binding C).

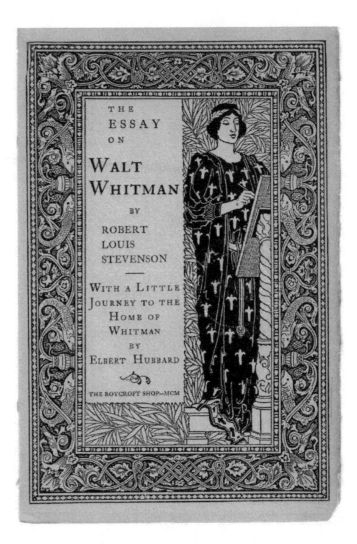

Title page of *The Essay on Walt Whitman,* by Robert
Louis Stevenson ([East Aurora, N.Y.]: The Roycroft
Shop, 1900).

NONFICTION

Although the Fales Collection is devoted primarily to the novel and other types of fiction, Fales actively collected works of nonfiction in order to illuminate the historical contexts in which the novelists were writing. He especially sought out biographies of the authors represented in his collection. For many of the novelists, there is at least one supporting work that helps provide a representative picture of Fales's favorite authors and the historical events which shaped their writings.

Child, Lydia Maria. *An Appeal in Favor of that Class of Americans Called Africans.* Boston: Allen & Ticknor, 1833. First ed. Rebound in brown buckram. In ink: "L. Vernon Briggs, Hanover Mass." This work, the first American book to argue for full racial equality and the immediate emancipation of the slaves, provided the abolitionist movement with "its first full-scale analysis of the slavery question" (Carolyn Karcher, Introduction to the 1996 edition, p. xxxii). While this highly controversial work elevated Child in the eyes of the abolitionist movement, it cost her deeply in her personal life. BAL 3116.

Emerson, Ralph Waldo. *English Traits*. Boston: Phillips, Sampson, & Co., 1856. First ed. Brown publisher's cloth. Book-label of Walter P. Chrysler, Jr. In ink: "A.W. Vintage." In *English Traits*, the transcendentalist Emerson records his first trips to England, in 1833 and 1847–48. After meeting literary and political notables such as Coleridge, Wordsworth, and Thomas Carlyle, he deemed the country "the best of actual nations." According to Howard Jones, "no better book by an American about Victorian England...has ever been written" (p. ix). American Firsts, p. 164; BAL 5226; Myerson A.24.1.a.

Godwin, William. *The Elopement of Percy Bysshe Shelley and Mary Wollstonecraft Godwin*. [Boston]: Privately printed, 1911. First ed. Tan publisher's cloth. Presentation copy: "Roswell Field with regards of W.K. Bixby, St. Louis 3/20/12." One of 200 copies printed for the collector William K. Bixby, this work includes the August 27, 1814, letter written by William Godwin to money lender and bill discounter John Taylor in reaction to his daughter's elopement with the poet Percy Shelley one month prior. Godwin tells Tyler that "[Shelley], a married man, has run away with my daughter. I cannot conceive of an event of more accumulated horror." DNB; NCBEL III 323.

Graves, Robert. *The Siege and Fall of Troy*. London: Cassell, 1962. First ed. Brown publisher's cloth. Immensely popular during World War II, Graves, a poet and novelist, was also a classicist. As Graves writes in his Introduction, "This is perhaps the first modern attempt to make the whole story [of the Trojan War]…into a single short book for boys and girls." On the dust-jacket of a copy not in the Fales Collection, the publishers claim that the illustrations by C. Walter Hodges, drawn specifically for this edition, are "a perfect complement to this most exciting of all adventure stories." DNB; Higginson, *Robert Graves* A102; NCBEL IV 203.

James, Henry. *"A Most Unholy Trade" Being Letters on the Drama by Henry James*. [Cambridge, Mass.]: The Scarab Press, Privately printed, 1923. First ed. Printed paper wrapper over flexible boards. One of only 100 copies printed, these four letters, part of a much larger correspondence with the publisher William Heinemann, contain James's impressions of Henrik Ibsen's drama "Little Eyolf." James proclaimed that "If Act III doesn't drop, it will be Ibsen's crown of glory." The frontispiece, an original drawing by John Singer Sargent, first appeared in *The Yellow Book* in 1894. American Firsts, p. 285; BAL 10710; Edel & Laurence C6; NCBEL III 997.

Le Gallienne, Richard. *The Romantic '90s*. London and New York: G.P. Putnam's Sons, 1926. First English ed. Blue publisher's cloth. In ink: "Henry from M.G. 16.8.27." Le Gallienne recaptures the atmosphere of the *fin de siècle* movement, one of incredible literary and cultural change, in this popular study. Himself a prominent figure of the period, Le Gallienne explains: "I have called the '90s 'romantic...because their representative writers and artists emphasized the modern determination to escape from the deadening thralldom of materialism and outworn conventions and to live life significantly." DNB; NCBEL IV 1063.

Mencken, H.L. *Menckeniana: A Schimpflexikon*. New York: Alfred A. Knopf, 1928. First ed., first limited printing. Publisher's bright orange-red vellum. During 1926, more than 500 editorials on the sayings and doings of the cultural critic Mencken were printed in the United States. His wife, Sarah Powell Haardt, also represented in the Collection, collected this unflattering material and grouped the insults into categories: the zoological, the genealogical, and the Freudian. *Menckeniana* "was the result and sold well" (Rodgers, p. 311). This particular copy is one of only eighty printed on Inomachi Japan vellum and inscribed by the author. Adler, p. 29; American Firsts, p. 361; Schrader A37.1.a.

Roosevelt, Theodore. *The Rough Riders.* New York: Charles Scribner's Sons, 1899. First ed. Olive publisher's cloth. This, Roosevelt's best-selling work, offers a classic account of his experiences during the Spanish-American War, including the Battle of San Juan Hill. In recounting the infamous regiment's formation, he notes, "[Leonard] Wood and I were speedily commissioned as Colonel and Lieutenant-Colonel of the First United States Volunteer Cavalry. This was the official title of the regiment, but for some reason or other the public promptly christened us the 'Rough Riders.'" American Firsts, p. 444; Wheelock, p. 11.

Seward, Anna. *Letters of Anna Seward Written Between the Years 1784 and 1807.* Edinburgh: Printed by George Ramsay for Archibald Constable & Co. [and 3 others], 1811. First ed., 6 vols. Half contemporary calf over marbled boards. Book-label of J. King, Appleford, Berks. Dubbed "the Swan of Lichfield," Seward engaged a number of notable eighteenth-century writers in her public letters. This set is extra-illustrated with a 1784 engraving of Major John Andre, the subject of Seward's most popular poem, "Monody on John Andre." The nineteenth-century practice of "extra illustration" involves adding independently acquired portraits, prints, and other matter to particular volumes. DNB; NCBEL II 682.

Stevenson, Robert Louis. *The Essay on Walt Whitman.* [East Aurora, N.Y.]: The Roycroft Shop, 1900. First ed. Publisher's red ooze calf with red silk doublures. This little-known essay by Stevenson on the work and legacy of "the good gray poet" was published with another essay by the Roycrofter Elbert Hubbard, "A Little Journey to the Home of Whitman." Stevenson writes that the key to Whitman's attitude is "to give a certain unity of ideal to the average population of America—to gather their activities about some conception of humanity that shall be central and normal, if only for the moment—the poet must portray that population as it is." Beinecke 119; Oscar Lion Collection, p. 69; Princeton University Library 15G.

Ward, Elizabeth Stuart Phelps. *What to Wear?* Boston: James R. Osgood & Co., 1873. First ed. Purple publisher's cloth. For Ward, the author of 57 books and hundreds of short stories, magazine articles, and poems, "writing was her primary avenue of feminist advocacy" (ANB). According to her publishers, she answered the question of *What to Wear?* "with sound sense, pungent sarcasm, wit, irony, and great *readableness*" (PW, July 5, 1873, p. 2) by proclaiming that "the present dress of woman is Bad Taste, Bad Hygiene, and Bad Morals." The *Boston Globe* agreed, noting that the work was distinguished by "true womanly feeling" (PW, July 5, 1873, p. 2). BAL 20874 (binding B).

Wells, H.G. *Floor Games*. London: Frank Palmer, 1911. First ed. Blue publisher's cloth with paper illustration of Wells's children pasted on front. Known today as the father of modern science fiction, Wells aimed to "guide humanity to a better world" (DNB). In *Floor Games*, however, he aims "merely to tell of the ordinary joys of playing with the floor." Toys are here divided into four main groups: "soldiers," "bricks," "boards and planks," and "clockwork railway rolling stock." A companion volume, *Little Wars* (1913), describes rules for toy-soldier war games. DNB; NCBEL IV 42; Wells 42.

Biography

Adams, Henry. *The Education of Henry Adams; An Autobiography*. Boston and New York: Houghton Mifflin Company, 1918. First ed. thus. Blue publisher's cloth. Winner of the 1919 Pulitzer Prize for Biography, *The Education of Henry Adams* topped Modern Library's list of the best English-language nonfiction books of the twentieth century. Adams offers incredible insight into late nineteenth-century intellectual and political life, noting that "no one has discussed what part of education has...turned out to be useful, and what not. This volume attempts to discuss it." American Firsts, p. 3; BAL 39.

Bryant, William Cullen. *A Discourse on the Life, Character and Genius of Washington Irving.* New York: G.P. Putnam, 1860. First ed., small paper. Green publisher's cloth. In ink: "H.N. Hoxie June 24th 1865." Bryant, a famed poet, abolitionist, and editor in chief of the *New York Evening News*, read this discourse aloud before the New York Historical Society at the New York Academy of Music on April 3, 1860—Irving's 77th birthday. One of the earliest posthumous celebrations of Irving's life, it was published less than a year after his death. American Firsts, p. 69; BAL 1668.

Gaskell, Elizabeth Cleghorn. *The Life of Charlotte Bronte.* London: Smith, Elder & Co., 1857. First ed. Dark-brown publisher's cloth (rebacked). In ink: "Mary Fuller." Although it fails to mention the more controversial aspects of Bronte's life, this, the first biography of Charlotte, has been acclaimed as a landmark in biography. A friend and fellow novelist, Gaskell was able to create a new, feminine form, recognizing that Bronte's "existence becomes divided into two parallel currents—her life as Currier Bell, the author; her life as Charlotte Bronte, the woman" (p. 49). DNB; NCBEL III 875; Parrish, *Victorian Lady Novelists*, p. 64; Sadleir 928; Symington, p. 58; Tinker 1058; Yablon 195.

Lindbergh, Charles. *"We."* New York and London: G.P. Putnam's Sons, 1927. First ed., first impression. Blue publisher's cloth. One of America's great aviators, Lindbergh was the first to fly nonstop from New York to Paris. Completed only a few months after his famed solo flight in the Spirit of St. Louis, which won Lindbergh $25,000, *"We,"* according to an early advertisement, "goes back in its recital to long before May 20, 1927, when a slim youth stood silhouetted beside his plane against the dawn, calmly awaiting the supreme test in his young life" (dust-jacket of a copy not in the Fales Collection). ANB; Luckett, p. 98.

Mitchell, Silas Weir. *The Youth of Washington Told in the Form of an Autobiography.* New York: The Century Co., 1904. First ed., large paper format. Blue-grey paper boards with white imitation vellum spine. Armorial bookplate of Elisha Rhodes Brown. Advertised by its publisher as "neither bald history nor pure fiction," Mitchell's work "imagines Washington, sitting down at Mount Vernon in his old age, and recording solely for his own eye the incidents and influences of his youth." While the larger historical facts are true, the fiction forms "a daring form of commentary" (PW, Oct. 8, 1904, p. 847.) American Firsts, p. 373; BAL 14223.

Stowe, Harriet Beecher. *Men of Our Times; or Leading Patriots of the Day.* Hartford, Conn.: Hartford Publishing Co., 1868. First ed., with second state title page. In ink: "Mrs. Mary C. Smith 1873." Abraham Lincoln once referred to Stowe as "the little women who wrote the book [*Uncle Tom's Cabin*] that started this great war" (ANB). Strongly influenced by her experiences during the Civil War, *Men of Our Times* is a collection of "sketches of some of the leading public men of our time." There are 18 sketches in all, including one of Lincoln and another of her brother, abolitionist Henry Ward Beecher. American Firsts, p. 482; ANB; BAL 19449; Hildreth, p. 92.

Caricature of Noel Coward from *Heroes and Heroines of Bitter Sweet,* by Max Beerbohm ([London: Leadlay, Ltd., 1931]).

DRAMA

As a collector of drama, Fales was especially interested in dramatic adaptations of previously published novels, and in plays and other dramatic works written by the novelists he collected. The plays included in this section are related to other novels in the Fales Collection through their subjects or their authorship. Fales had a particular interest in comedies, which are highlighted here.

Baldwin, James. *Blues for Mister Charlie: A Play*. New York: Dial Press, 1964. First ed. Black publisher's cloth. Growing up in Harlem, Baldwin was well aware of the extent to which African-Americans were subjected to racial oppression. Based loosely on the 1955 murder of Emmett Till in Mississippi, the play, in Baldwin's own words, "takes place in Plaguetown, U.S.A., now. The plague is race, the plague is our concept of Christianity: and this raging plague has the power to destroy every human relationship.... We are walking in terrible darkness here, and this is one man's attempt to bear witness to the reality and the power of light." Patterson, p. 49.

Barrie, J.M. *Der Tag: A Play*. London, New York, Toronto: Hodder & Stoughton, 1914. First ed. Dark-grey buckram over lighter-grey boards. Armorial bookplate of the Viscount Esher. Barrie, creator of Peter Pan, first produced this drama at the London Coliseum on December 21, 1914. Although Barrie had great success as a dramatist, this war play was released to hostile reviews. London's *Athenaeum* claimed, "It is as inadequate in its purpose of presenting to us the cause and effect of the present war as a tin whistle would be were it used to sound a cavalry charge" (*Athenaeum*, Dec. 26, 1914, p. 674). Cutler 71; Garland 42; NCBEL III 1190.

Beerbohm, Max. *Heroes and Heroines of Bitter Sweet.* [London: Leadlay, Ltd., 1931]. First ed. Eight separate sheets of light-grey cardboard, in portfolio of grey boards, with white vellum spine. This collection of six portrait-size caricatures of characters from Noel Coward's operetta *Bitter Sweet* (1929) was created by the famed artist to commemorate the show's production in London's West End theatre. It is one of 900 copies. Beerbohm, in his introductory note, writes that "Sentiment is out of fashion. Yet 'Bitter Sweet,' which is nothing if not sentimental, has not been a dead failure." Gallatin & Oliver 30; NCBEL IV 1002.

Collins, Wilkie. *The Moonstone: A Dramatic Story in Three Acts. Altered from the Novel for Performance on the Stage.* London: Charles Dickens & Evans, 1877. First ed. Later buff paper wrappers. Collins, best known for his detective novels, met with some success as a playwright in the 1870s. However, the theatrical adaptation of his 1868 classic of detective fiction was "somewhat coldly received" (*The Academy,* Sept. 22, 1877, p. 304). According to an early reviewer, the lesson of the play is "don't give up smoking, or you will walk in your sleep, and steal the jewels of your lover" (Parrish, *Wilkie Collins,* pp. 75–76). The play was performed for only two months, and surviving copies are scarce. Craigie 76; DNB; NCBEL III 925; Wolff 1368b.

Davidson, John. *Plays*. London: E. Mathews & J. Lane; Chicago: Stone & Kimball, 1894. First ed. Lavender publisher's cloth. Bookseller's ticket of R.H. Blackwell, Oxford. Davidson, deemed "a child of the age" (May, p. 98), followed the success of his poetic volume *Fleet Street Eclogues* (1893, also in Fales) by publishing this collected edition of his plays. The plays were an attempt to "discover the dramatic form of the future" (Nelson, p. 233), a goal which Davidson states outright in the preface to his *Scaramouch in Naxos*—the play that became the inspiration for the volume's now famous frontispiece created by Aubrey Beardsley. Kramer 17; NCBEL III 620; Samuels Lasner 58.

Gregory, Lady Augusta. *The Image: A Play in Three Acts*. Dublin: Maunsel & Co., Ltd., 1910. First ed. Modern buff paper boards. Deemed "the greatest living Irishwoman" and "the charwoman of the Abbey" by Bernard Shaw (DNB), Lady Gregory was a champion of the theatre she helped W.B. Yeats establish in Dublin. At the age of fifty, Lady Gregory suddenly emerged as a dramatist herself, and from 1902 through 1927 she wrote some three dozen plays. This one, like many of her later works, is "invested in myth-making functions" and centers on "the transformative power of a hidden 'heart secret'" (DNB). NCBEL III 1940.

Kemble, Frances Anne (Fanny). *Francis the First. An Historical Drama.* London: John Murray, 1832. First ed. Marbled paper boards (rebacked). Armorial bookplate of Henry B. Anthony. Born into a prominent acting family, Kemble "reigned for several years as the brightest of the young actresses of her day" (DNB) before beginning her career as a writer. One of two historical plays she wrote and appeared in, *Francis the First* "was exciting, the heroine stabbed herself in the end; the costumes were lovely, and there was a last scene in the Certosa at Pavia, with troops of monks singing *de profundis* in pitch darkness, so drenched in gloom that Fanny wept as she wrote" (Armstrong, p. 54). NCBEL III 530.

MacLeish, Archibald. *The Fall of the City: A Verse Play for Radio.* New York and Toronto: Farrar & Rinehart, Inc., 1937. First ed. Publisher's orange paper boards. MacLeish, who won three Pulitzer Prizes and served as Librarian of Congress, "remains notable as one of those who influenced the development of modern poetry" (ANB). MacLeish felt that poetry should be "public speech," especially in tumultuous time likes the thirties, and in this work he speaks out against the rise of fascism. Narrated by Orson Welles, this was the first verse play written for radio. American Firsts, p. 344; Donaldson, p. 268; Mizener 49.

O'Neill, Eugene. *The Emperor Jones*. Cincinnati: Stewart Kidd Company, 1921. First separate ed. Printed paper wrappers. Winner of the 1936 Nobel Prize in Literature, O'Neill was one of the first playwrights to introduce aspects of Realism into American drama. *The Emperor Jones* is one of his major experimental works and his first box-office hit. The drama follows Brutus Jones, a "larger-than life black American" (Patterson, p. 135) who becomes emperor of a West Indian island, then prepares for a revolt by the natives. This was the first play to offer a leading role to a black actor in a mainly white company. American Firsts, p. 401; Atkinson A15-II-I.

Saroyan, William. *The Cave Dwellers; A Play*. London: Faber & Faber, 1959. First English ed. Green publisher's cloth. Saroyan was an Armenian-American, and his fiction, essays, memoirs, and plays were "among the earliest expressions of a specifically ethnic voice in American literature" (ANB). One review claimed that this "allegorical-philosophical-existentialist fantasy, is about as curious a play as can be unearthed" (*New York Times*, May 5, 2002, section WC, p. 14). In the preface, Saroyan tells his reader that "the human race is still as fearfully sick as it was when it began…. [As] a little of my share, I wrote this play. Enjoy it, it's good for you." Kherdian 163.

Swinburne, Algernon Charles. *Erechtheus: A Tragedy*.
London: Chatto & Windus, 1876. First ed. Blue publisher's cloth.   A poet of the decadent school,
Swinburne was described by Oscar Wilde as a "brag-
gart in matters of vice" (Everett). While many readers
and critics admired Swinburne, some found *Erechtheus*
too abstract and severe in outlook. Swinburne described the work to a friend as "a Greek tragedy, which
I mean to be more purely Hellenic and perhaps more
universal in its relation to human thought than was 'At-
lanta' [1865]. The fusion of lyric with dramatic form
gives the highest type of poetry I know" (Wise, *Swinburne*, p. 62). DNB; NCBEL III 572.

Comedy

Bird, Robert Montgomery. *The City Looking Glass*. *A Philadelphia Comedy, in Five Acts*. New York: Printed for the
Colophon, 1933. First ed. Red publisher's cloth. After
practicing medicine for only a year, Bird became a successful novelist and playwright. *The City Looking Glass*,
published here for the first time in an edition of 465
copies by the Pynson Printers, was written in July 1828.
Arthur Hobson Quinn describes the work as "a picture
of both gallant and depraved, of fortunate and unfor-
tunate characters, as they lived in Philadelphia over a
century ago." American Firsts, p. 56; BAL 1177.

Lennox, Charlotte. *Old City Manners. A Comedy.* London: Printed for T. Becket, 1775. First ed. Modern brown paper wrappers. Lennox is best remembered today for her novel *The Female Quixote* (1752) and for her associations with Samuel Johnson and members of his literary circle. *Old City Manners*, first performed November 9, 1775, in Drury-Lane, is a "very judiciously altered" version of *Eastern Hoe* (1605), by George Chapman, Ben Jonson, and John Marston, a satirical play about social customs in early modern London. Produced by David Garrick, it ran for seven nights and was later deemed "an entertaining and well-constructed comedy." (Both quotations are from the *Morning Chronicle*, Nov. 10, 1775, second page.) DNB; ESTC t10816; NCBEL II 848; Nicoll, p. 281.

Longfellow, Henry Wadsworth. *The Spanish Student. A Play, in Three Acts.* Cambridge: Published by John Owen, 1843. First ed. Half contemporary morocco over marbled boards. Before winning acclaim as a poet, Longfellow was, beginning in 1834, Smith Professor of French and Spanish at Harvard. After reading the comedies of Spanish dramatist Torres Naharro in 1840, Longfellow wrote in his journal: "A good idea! Yes, I will write a comedy,—'The Spanish Student!'" (Livingston, *Longfellow*, p. 33). The play was first published in *Graham's Magazine* in 1842. American Firsts, p. 324; BAL 12071.

Shaw, George Bernard. *Passion, Poison, and Petrification, or The Fatal Gazogene.* London: Anthony Treherne, 1905. First ed. Printed paper wrappers. This work first appeared in the ill-fated *Christmas Annual* started by the illustrator Harry Furniss in 1905. After acquiring Shaw's manuscript at a 1905 charity auction, collector Robert Hoe, under the misconception that his purchase included the copyright, authorized the play to be printed in book form. Shaw took legal action in an attempt to prevent its publication, noting that the play was "a silly little burlesque melodrama...twelve minutes long, to play in a booth at a charity bazaar. It is quite impossible for me to permit such a thing to be printed and published as if it were a serious piece of work" (Laurence A69, B33). Gordon, *Bernard Shaw*, p. 27; NCBEL III 1171.

Sheridan, Frances. *The Discovery. A Comedy.* London: Printed for T. Davies [and 4 others], 1763. First ed. Contemporary marbled paper wrappers cased in later brick paper wrapper. After publishing *Memoirs of Miss Sidney Bidulph* (1761), Sheridan turned from fiction to the theatre. The result was this comedy, which pleased David Garrick, who staged it at Drury Lane on February 3, 1763. John O'Keefe proclaimed that Sheridan's work "gave great delight and the success was perfect" (DNB). It played to full houses for 17 nights and was later revived by Aldous Huxley in 1924. Huxley's adaptation is also in the Fales Collection. ESTC t943; NCBEL II 859; Nicoll, p. 305; Rothschild 1840.

Wilde, Oscar. *Lady Windermere's Fan: A Play About a Good Woman*. London: Elkin Mathews & John Lane, 1893. First ed. Mauve publisher's cloth. Bookplate of Aubrey Ward. In ink: "Christmas 1893." The story of Lady Windermere's elopement with Lord Darlington, this was Wilde's first dramatic success. Three years later, he had reached the "absolute summit of the English theater" (Phillips et al., p. 104). The epitome of aestheticism and decadence in the 1890s, Wilde, as described by his close friend Richard Le Gallienne, "made dying Victorianism laugh at itself, and it may be said to have died of laughter" (p. 270). DNB; Mason 357; NCBEL III 1183; Tinker 2301.

Illustration facing page 272 of *My Strangest Case*, by
Guy Boothby (London: Ward, Lock & Co., 1902).

20TH-CENTURY BRITISH FICTION

After concentrating on the novel of the eighteenth and nineteenth centuries, Fales turned his attention to twentieth-century fiction. He actively acquired works from the Edwardian period as well as Modernist works published during and after World War II. He was particularly interested in detective fiction. The four "queens of crime" from the golden age of crime fiction—Agatha Christie, Margery Allingham, Dorothy Sayers, and Ngaio Marsh—are represented in depth.

Beckett, Samuel. *From an Abandoned Work*. London: Faber & Faber, 1958. First ed. Printed paper wrappers. This work is a fragment of an unfinished novel written ca. 1955. When the Nobel laureate was asked why the story ends abruptly, he responded "there was just no more to be said" (Federman & Fletcher 33.2). A hostile reviewer *did* have more to say, proclaiming "here...is another proof that mere authenticity, however 'true to life,' does not suffice for artistic creation" (TLS, Dec. 26, 1958, p. 752.) DNB; NCBEL IV 886.

Bennett, Arnold. *Riceyman Steps*. London: Cassell & Co., Ltd., 1923. First ed. Green publisher's cloth. A novelist, short-story writer, dramatist, critic, essayist, and journalist, Bennett was one of the more popular Edwardian authors. With J.B. Pinker as his agent, Bennett went on to become one of the highest-paid writers of his age. *Riceyman Steps* chronicles a year in the life of Henry Earlforward, a secondhand bookshop owner in the Clerkenwell area of London. The story was inspired by Bennett's own visit to a family-owned Southampton bookshop in the summer of 1921. DNB; Emery 35; Gordon, *Arnold Bennett*, pp. 7, 48; NCBEL IV 430.

Conrad, Joseph. *Lord Jim. A Tale*. Edinburgh and London: William Blackwood & Sons, 1900. First ed., first impression. Light-green publisher's cloth. Like Conrad's critically acclaimed novel *Heart of Darkness* (1899), *Lord Jim* was originally published as a serial in *Blackwood's Magazine*. This story of a young British seaman named Jim, according to T.F. Powys, "goes into the unknown places of the earth, it delves under its obscure surface, showing the horror, the hunger, that is in the soul of man" (Keating, p. 70). Arthur Symons further professed that it "is more than a novel; it is life itself, and it a criticism of life. It is *Lord Jim* in which [Conrad's] genius has attained its zenith" (Keating, p. 72). DNB; Keating 25–26; NCBEL IV 397; Smith, *Joseph Conrad* 5; Wise, *Conrad* 7.

Du Maurier, Daphne. *Rebecca*. London: Victor Gollancz, 1938. First ed. Black publisher's cloth. The granddaughter of George Du Maurier, whose best-selling *Trilby* (1894) is in the Fales Collection, Daphne was a successful novelist in her own right. Intended as a psychological study of jealously based on her own feelings, *Rebecca* "was hailed as a romantic novel in the tradition of *Jane Eyre*" (DNB). An instant hit, this modern Gothic tale sold 2.8 million copies by 1965 and was the basis for the 1940 Oscar-winning film directed by Albert Hitchcock and starring Joan Fontaine. NCBEL IV 566.

Galsworthy, John. *In Chancery*. London: William Heineman, 1920. First ed., first issue. Green publisher's cloth. Bookplate of Millicent W. Smyth. Galsworthy, winner of the 1932 Nobel Prize in Literature, is perhaps best remembered for his Forsyte Saga, a series of three novels and two interludes published between 1906 and 1921. *In Chancery*, the second novel in the trilogy, is a "study of the effects on English society of the imperial vision and the South African War" (DNB). Writer and poet Katherine Mansfield called it a "fascinating, brilliant book" (DNB). Marrot, p. 31; NCBEL IV 580.

Greene, Graham. *The Man Within*. London: William Heinemann Ltd., 1929. First ed., first impression. Black publisher's cloth. In 1926 Greene was appointed a sub-editor at *The Times*. In his spare time, he wrote his first novel *The Man Within*, an historical romance about the smuggling trade on the Sussex coast in the early 1800s. Published when Greene was only twenty-five, this novel sold 13,000 hardcover copies. Emboldened by his newfound critical and commercial success, Greene soon left his editing job and became a writer full-time. DNB; Miller 7a; NCBEL IV 504; Wise & Hill A2; Wobbe A2.

Huxley, Aldous. *Time Must Have a Stop.* London: Chatto & Windus, 1945. First English ed. Light-blue publisher's cloth. This complex story involves the search for meaning in the lives of two teenage boys during World War II. The physical volume is notable because it demonstrates the lower production standards imposed by the Book Production War Economy Agreement. This novel, like all others published in the U.K. during the War, was produced on "thin, low quality paper covered with small, closely set type" (Suarez, p. 189). Ironically, the making of Huxley's "response to a world at war" (DNB) was shaped by the war itself. Eschelbach & Shober 61; NCBEL IV 610.

Joyce, James. *Two Tales of Shem and Shaun. Fragments from Work in Progress.* London: Faber & Faber, 1932. First English ed. Pale green boards. Prior to its publication in book form in 1939, *Finnegans Wake* was known as *Work in Progress.* This booklet includes "The Mookse and the Gripes" and "The Ondt and the Grasshopper," stories which reappear in parts I and III of the novel. Publishing parts of *Finnegans Wake* separately in journals and booklets, starting in 1924, "gave Joyce the opportunity to revise his work endlessly, and to evolve the idea of the modern novel as a 'work in progress'" (DNB). NCBEL IV 446; Slocum & Cahoon A37.

Lawrence, D.H. *The First Lady Chatterley*. New York: Dial Press, 1944. First ed. of first manuscript version. Blue-grey publisher's cloth. Lawrence wrote three versions of his controversial *Lady Chatterley's Lover*, and only the third version (Florence, Italy, 1928) was published in his lifetime. This, the first version, was published after the author's death in 1930. In her assessment of the manuscript, Esther Forbes wrote, "I think the first draft is Lawrence at his best with much of *Sons and Lovers'* warmth, accuracy, humanity…. In this first draft he is a novelist—pure and simple." DNB; NCBEL IV 484, Roberts A42g.

Sackville-West, Vita. *The Edwardians*. London: Printed by Leonard & Virginia Woolf The Hogarth Press, 1930. First trade ed., first impression. Orange publisher's cloth. In a 1929 letter to her close friend and sometime lover Virginia Woolf, Sackville-West recounted that in producing this satire of Edwardian high society, she attempted to "remember…the impression of waste and extravagance which assailed one the moment one entered the doors of [her childhood] house" (DeSalvo & Leaska, p. 338). Part of the aristocracy herself, Sackville-West was well equipped to pen what Carl Van Doren deemed "The True and Delightful history of an era and a class" (Cross & Ravenscroft-Hulme A.20a). DNB; NCBEL IV 336; Woolmer 235B.

Waugh, Evelyn. *Scoop: A Novel About Journalists.* London: Chapman & Hall, 1938. First ed., first issue with the "8" in the publication date indistinct. Red and black marbled publisher's cloth. This blistering satire of sensationalist journalism, featuring fictional columnist William Boot, remains one of Waugh's most popular books. In 1957, the author described *Scoop* as "a light satire of modern journalism" (Stannard, p. 472), an effort to expose the pretensions of foreign correspondents. Davis et al. 15; DNB; NCBEL IV 765.

Wodehouse, P.G. *The Inimitable Jeeves.* London: Hubert Jenkins, 1923. First ed. Green publisher's cloth. This short story collection by Wodehouse, "the greatest of all English humorists" (DNB), features the escapades of his best-known characters—Bertie Wooster and his valet Reginald Jeeves. A prefatory advertisement titled "What this book is about" reads: "When either Bertie Wooster or his friends found themselves in the soup or in dangerous proximity to the tureen, the instinct of one and all was to turn to Jeeves—Bertie's man.... In this volume are told some of Jeeves's more remarkable achievements." Heinemann & Bensen A30A; Jasen 31; NCBEL IV 779.

Woolf, Virginia. *The Waves.* London: Published by Leonard & Virginia Woolf at the Hogarth Press, 1931. First ed. Purple publisher's cloth (rebacked). In ink: "J. Fraser Nicol." *The Waves,* which deals with the lives of six early Bloomsbury Group writers, is regarded as Woolf's most daring, experimental, and personal work. In the Introduction to the 1990 edition, Angelica Garnett claims that "strictly speaking, it is not a novel: it is an autobiographical account of certain relationships, ideas and experiences, with an attempt to define the subsequently perceived values" (p. xi). Connolly 70; DNB; Kirkpatrick A16a; NCBEL IV 473; Woolmer 279.

Crime and Detective Fiction

Allingham, Margery. *The Tiger in the Smoke*. London: Chatto & Windus, 1952. First ed. Red publisher's cloth, with dust-jacket tipped in. Allingham is notable for her memorable recurring characters, "who grow in depth as her career proceeds" (DNB). *The Tiger in the Smoke*, where London is "the Smoke," features detective Albert Campion, the most important of these characters. This work, "with its killer on the loose in fog-bound London, its surreal touches, and its intense drama of good and evil" (DNB), is Allingham's most critically acclaimed novel.

Boothby, Guy. *My Strangest Case*. London: Ward, Lock & Co., 1902. First ed. Blue publisher's cloth. Toward the end of his life Boothby, an Australian novelist, wrote sensational and dramatic stories at an exceptionally rapid rate. Although these works were widely read, they "had small faculty for characterization or literary style" (DNB). In this story, the action shifts from China to London, Paris, and Italy (PW, July 6, 1901, p. 20). "Three Englishmen find jewels in Burma; one of them robs the others, and is hunted about England and the Continent by a very incompetent detective" (TLS, Mar. 28, 1902, p. 87).

Chesterton, G.K. *The Innocence of Father Brown.* London: Cassell & Co., Ltd., 1911. First ed. Red publisher's cloth. Bookseller's ticket of Corvinus Bookshop, Bristol. This collection marks the first appearance of Father Brown, the "insignificant-seeming little Roman Catholic priest" (DNB) who solved mysteries and crimes using his deep insight into human nature and the criminal mentality in particular. The best-known of Chesterton's fictional characters would come to appear in four additional short story collections; three of which are in the Fales Collection in first edition. The Collection also includes more than 50 other works by the imposing Chesterton in first and early editions. NCBEL IV 1024; Sullivan 24.

Christie, Agatha. *Five Little Pigs.* London: Published for the Crime Club by Collins, 1942. First English ed. Red-orange publisher's cloth, with dust-jacket tipped in. In *Five Little Pigs*, first published in the U.S. under the title *Murder in Retrospect,* famed detective Hercule Poirot examines "the evidence afresh" 16 years after Caroline Crale was first convicted for the murder of her husband Amyas. TLS concluded that "no crime enthusiast will object that the story of how the painter died has to be told many times, for this…demonstrates the author's uncanny skill. The answer to the riddle is brilliant" (TLS, Jan. 16, 1943, p. 29). NCBEL IV 553; Osborne, p. 245.

Marsh, Ngaio. *Swing, Brother, Swing*. London: Published for the Crime Club by Collins, 1949. First ed. Red-orange publisher's cloth. Marsh rose to prominence in the 1930s when she expanded the conventions of crime fiction beyond that of the "locked-door" mysteries. She was instead "more interested in character and social manners than plot" (DNB). During "Gala Night at the Metronome, gayest of all the fashionable night-clubs," Chief-Inspector Roderick Alleyn of Scotland Yard must unwittingly mix business with pleasure after witnessing the murder of Carlos Rivera, the piano-accordionist of the Breezy Bellairs.

Sayers, Dorothy L. *Gaudy Night*. London: Victor Gollancz Ltd., 1935. First ed. Black publisher's cloth. In *Gaudy Night*, scholar and author Sayers "combines a sensational detective story with a genuine English novel" (DNB). Featuring Lord Peter Wimsey and Harriet Vane, the novel takes place at Harriet's alma mater, Shrewsbury College, Oxford, where she returns for the annual Gaudy celebrations. Fictional Shrewsbury College is based on Sayers's own Somerville College, and women's right to an academic education is central to the plot. Gilbert A21 a.1; NCBEL IV 731.

Wallace, Edgar. *The Four Just Men*. London: Tallis Press, 1905. First ed. Yellow publisher's cloth. *The Four Just Men* was both a financial disaster and one of Wallace's most enduring novels. In this locked-room mystery, the case was left unsolved. Readers were instead invited to send in their own solutions, and a £500 prize was offered to the person who solved the mystery. Wallace neglected to state that only *one* winner would receive the prize, however. Having financed the novel himself, he was forced to declare bankruptcy. In this copy, the rare solution slip is still intact, meaning that its original owner was perhaps not interested in solving this interactive mystery. DNB; Lofts & Adley B61; NCBEL IV 754.

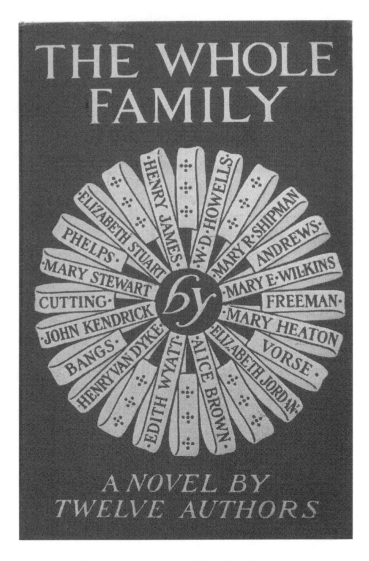

Cover of *The Whole Family: A Novel by Twelve Authors*
(New York and London: Harper & Brothers Publishers, 1908).

20TH-CENTURY AMERICAN FICTION

Fales began seriously building his American fiction collection in the late 1950s. He once noted that "the American section of the collection provides a good picture, from Cooper down to the moderns" (New York University, *Bulletin*, Society for the Libraries, Winter 1959). Manhattan College's collection is particularly strong in Realist novels, especially those that comment on widespread social change. Another strength is the short story, a genre that began to take hold in the early twentieth century with the rise of high-profile literary periodicals such as *Harper's Magazine*. Short stories were often published first in periodicals, then later collected in book form.

Dos Passos, John. *The Big Money*. New York: Harcourt, Brace & Co., 1936. First ed. Blue publisher's cloth. *The Big Money* is the third and final novel in Dos Passos's U.S.A. Trilogy—the first two being *The 42nd Parallel* (1930), also in the Fales Collection, and *1919* (1932). The trilogy, known for its biting criticism of American attitudes and life in the early twentieth century, has since become a landmark of American modernism. *The Big Money*, remarked PW, "represents the fullest expression of Dos Passos's brilliant powers of rapid, revealing story-telling" (PW, June 20, 1936, p. 2426). American Firsts, p. 148; ANB; Potter 26; Sanders A36-1.

Dreiser, Theodore. *The "Genius."* New York: John Lane Company; London: John Lane, The Bodley Head, 1915. First ed., first issue. Red publishers' cloth. The New York Society for the Suppression of Vice deemed *The Genius*, Dreiser's most autobiographical novel, so obscene that it was "unfit to read." They successfully pressured the publishers to discontinue its circulation. In response, Dreiser claimed, "Some of the men…decided that the book didn't come up to their ideas of high moral standards" (*New York Times*, Aug. 21, 1916, p. 20). After a series of legal battles, the book was finally reissued in 1923. American Firsts, p. 151; ANB; McDonald 7.

Faulkner, William. *The Hamlet*. New York: Random House, 1940. First trade ed., first printing. Black publisher's cloth. In ink: "Peter Martin." Members of the "fantastic and fascinating family named Snopes" (PW, Mar. 9, 1940, p. 1065) were recurring characters throughout all of Faulkner's early fiction. Recounting the story of how Flem Snopes and his family descended upon Frenchman's Bend and seized it "with their tentacles, octopus fashion," (*Detroit News*, Apr. 7, 1940, p. 81), this is the first of the Snopes novels. *The Town* (1957) and *The Mansion* (1959) complete the trilogy. American Firsts, p. 171, ANB; Massey 56l.

Harris, Joel Chandler. *Told by Uncle Remus: New Stories of the Old Plantation*. New York: McClure, Phillips & Co., 1905. First ed. Maroon publisher's buckram. Bookseller's ticket of W.B. Clarke Co., Boston. Published "a generation since the first Uncle Remus stories appeared to delight the young folks" (PW, Sept. 30, 1905, p. 777), this work exposed readers to the antics of Brer Rabbit, Brer Fox, Mr. Dog, Sis Hen, and Sis Cow. Harris, "with his sharp ear for African American narrative structure and dialect voice...brought the narrative genius of ante-bellum African American culture before a wider audience" (Scofield, p. 184). American Firsts, p. 213; BAL 7156.

Hough, Emerson. *The Mississippi Bubble*. Indianapolis: The Bowen-Merrill Company, 1902. First ed., BAL's printing B. Green publisher's cloth. Book-label of Arthur Swann. Bookseller's ticket of Fred Lockley, Portland, Oregon. This historical novel revolves around the story of Scottish economist John Law (1671–1729) and the Mississippi Bubble, an economic bubble of speculative investment in the French colony of Louisiana. Described by *The Critic* as "one of the best novels that has come out of America in many a day" (PW, May 31, 1902, p. 1197), this book launched Hough's career in fiction. American Firsts, p. 263; ANB; BAL 9318 (later binding).

Howells, William Dean, et al. *The Whole Family: A Novel by Twelve Authors*. New York and London: Harper & Brothers Publishers, 1908. First ed. Blue publisher's cloth. This collectively authored novel was meant to "exemplify the principles of Howellsian realism by depicting an archetypal American family 'in middling circumstances, of average culture and experiences'" (Crowley, pp. 96–99). Each of the twelve authors contributed a chapter written from the first-person viewpoint of one member of the extended family. When Mary E. Wilkins' chapter discarded the "Spinster Stereotype" to cast Miss Elizabeth Talbert as a "sexually vital woman," Howell's unique concept became a "catastrophe" (Crowley, pp. 96–99). American Firsts, p. 273; BAL 779, 6389, 9790, 10667, 20995; Edel & Laurence B27; Gibson & Arms 08-C.

Lewis, Sinclair. *Babbitt*. New York: Harcourt, Brace & Co., 1922. First ed., first state. The novel's protagonist George F. Babbitt is, in the words of Lewis, "all of us Americans at 46, prosperous, but worried, wanting—passionately—to seize something more than motor cars and a house *before it's too late*" (Smith, *From Main Street to Stockholm*, p. 59). Controversial for its critiques of "the spiritual lacks of the average business man" (High Spots, p. 51), *Babbitt* proved influential in the decision to award Lewis the 1930 Nobel Prize in Literature—the first ever won by an American. American Firsts, p. 311; ANB; Pastore 8.

Miller, Henry. *Black Spring*. New York: Grove Press, 1963. First American ed. Black publisher's cloth over grey marbled paper boards. First published in Paris in 1936, Miller's *Black Spring*, dedicated to his lover Anaïs Nin, is "a vivid sequence of sketches, personal recollections, and dreams" (ANB) that take Miller from his childhood in Brooklyn to the literary world of Paris. With the publication of this work, Miller's three most important Paris books—*Black Spring, Tropic of Cancer* (1934), and *Tropic of Capricorn* (1939)—were all widely available in America. Shifreen & Jackson A12.

Poole, Ernest. *His Family*. New York: The Macmillan Company, 1917. First ed. Blue publisher's cloth. While Poole never matched the success of his first novel, *The Harbor* (1915), this, his second, won the Pulitzer Prize for Fiction in 1918—the first such prize ever awarded. Set in New York, it was proclaimed "the most humanly appealing romance of American life in a number of years" (PW, May 12, 1917, p. 1551). While H.L. Mencken claimed that Poole was "A Bad Novelist,", Carl Van Doren was closer to the critical consensus when he deemed Poole's two novels "works of honest art and excellent documents upon a generation" (ANB).

Steinbeck, John. *Cannery Row*. London: William Heinemann Ltd., 1945. First English ed. Orange-yellow
publisher's cloth. Steinbeck, winner of the 1962 Nobel
Prize in Literature, is perhaps best known for his novel
The Grapes of Wrath (1939). *Cannery Row* focuses on the
acceptance of life as it is—on both the exuberance of
community and the loneliness of the individual. Susan
Shillinglaw described the story as a "timeless fable, hi-
larious and tender, of some lovable people in a
California coast town." The sequel, *Sweet Thursday*
(1954), is also in the Fales Collection. Goldstone &
Payne A22c.

Tarkington, Booth. *Alice Adams*. Garden City, New York:
Doubleday, Page & Co., 1921. First ed., first state. Red
publisher's cloth. Tarkington was famous, affluent,
and critically acclaimed during his lifetime, but his reputation has since faded. This, probably his best novel,
was winner of the 1922 Pulitzer Prize for Fiction. It is
"the story of a middle-class girl who, stripped of her
romantic illusions, come to terms with life" (ANB). The
1935 film adaptation created a memorable role for actress Katherine Hepburn, who played Alice. American
Firsts, p. 490; Russo, p. 53.

Wharton, Edith. *The Fruit of the Tree*. New York: Charles
Scribner's Sons, 1907. First ed. Red publisher's cloth.
In ink: "A. Neristadt Chappaqua 1909." Designated
The Book of the Year by *Publishers Weekly*, this novel
deals directly with problems of social and personal life.
It "culminates in the ending of cruel suffering, by an
overdose of morphine, sympathetically administered
by the trained nurse [Justine Brent]" (PW, Jan. 25, 1907,
p. 132). With *The Age of Innocence* (1920), Wharton be-
came the first woman to win the Pulitzer Prize for
Fiction. American Firsts, p. 517; ANB; Garrison
A14.1.a1 (binding B).

Williams, Tennessee. *The Roman Spring of Mrs. Stone.*
New York: New Directions, 1950. First trade ed. Black
publisher's cloth. This work is the first of only a few
novels written by Williams, "whose highly popular
works stretched the boundaries of what could be
shown and discussed on the stage and screen" (ANB).
The publisher stated that the book was "certain to be a
bestseller—The story of an American actress in Europe—all the power of 'Streetcar Named Desire'—all
the insight of 'Glass Menagerie'" (PW, May 27, 1950, p.
30). This story of an American woman and her aban-
donment in Rome became a 1961 hit film starring
Vivien Leigh and Warren Beatty. ANB; Crandell A91.b.

Wright, Richard. *Native Son.* New York and London:
Harper & Brothers, 1940. First ed. Second state binding of grey publisher's cloth. Regarded by Maxwell
Whiteman as "the most articulate expression of the
psychological problems which lead to violence and
brutality yet to be put into the form of a novel" (p. 48),
Native Son was the first bestselling novel by a black
American writer and made Wright the "most respected
and wealthiest black writer in America" (ANB). Divided into three parts, this novel tells the story of
Bigger Thomas, an edgy nineteen-year-old growing up
in Chicago's South Side in the 1930s.

The Short Story

Boyle, Kay. *The White Horses of Vienna*. New York: Harcourt, Brace & Co., 1936. First ed. Light-blue publisher's cloth. A writer, educator, and political activist, Boyle wrote 40 books in her lifetime, including 14 novels and 8 volumes of poetry. *The White Horses of Vienna* won her the O. Henry Award for outstanding short story in 1935. Set in Austria in the early 1930s, this collection's title story "is exemplary of much of Boyle's writing, for it articulates an urgent need for art to engage with political and social issues" (ANB). Boyle remains an important figure in American literary modernism. Chambers A11a.

Crane, Stephen. *Whilomville Stories*. New York and London: Harper & Brothers, 1900. First ed. Green publisher's cloth. Book-stamp of A.B. Clayton. Crane, best remembered for his Civil War novel *The Red Badge of Courage* (1895), portrays "the vicissitudes of American childhood" (ANB) in these 13 stories set in the mythical town of Whilomville. *The Boston Herald* noted that illustrator Peter Newell, "is in his element in illustrating a book of funny stories like these, and the volume may be commended to any one in search of amusement" (*Boston Herald*, Aug. 25, 1900, p. 7). American Firsts, p. 129; BAL 4089; Stallman, p. 231; Starett 19; Wright, *1876–1900* 1259.

Kerouac, Jack. *Lonesome Traveler*. New York: McGraw-Hill, 1960. First ed. Half black and brown publisher's cloth over paper boards. Kerouac, a literary iconoclast, was a pioneer of the Beat Generation best remembered for his novels *The Dharma Bums* (1958) and *On the Road* (1957). Describing this collection of short stories and sketches, the publisher wrote "The king of the beatniks holds forth on his travels and adventures from Mexico to Paris. Full of the old Kerouac flair for variety and shock—should set the public talking, with enthusiasm or with rage" (PW, July 25, 1960, p. 4). Charters A13a.

London, Jack. *Moon-Face and Other Stories*. New York: The Macmillan Company; London: Macmillan & Co., Ltd., 1906. First published ed. Blue publisher's cloth. In ink: "Carl Jacobsen." Bookseller's ticket of Eureka Book Shop. For London, author of *The Call of the Wild* (1903), "the short story was an ideal form...since his major preoccupations—above all the preoccupation with crises of survival—lent themselves to short and concentrated treatment" (ANB). Of the eight stories in this collection, the best-known is "Planchette," a ghost story in which the spirit of a woman's dead father returns to kill her lover. American Firsts, p. 318; BAL 11895; Scofield, p. 121; Woodbridge 43.

Porter, Katherine Anne. *The Leaning Tower and Other Stories*. New York: Harcourt, Brace & Co., 1944. First ed.
Cream publisher's cloth. Porter is remembered primarily for the "restrained style and evocative symbolism of
her short stories and novellas" (ANB). "The Leaning
Tower," the title work in this, her third major collection, is a "fine but austere story of prewar Berlin"
(ANB). The collection is also notable for a sequence of
stories entitled The Old Order—especially the final
story, "The Grave," in which "a young girl first experiences birth and death" (Scofield, p. 173). Schwartz, p.
13; Waldrip & Bauer A9a.

Porter, William Sydney. (O. Henry.) *Let Me Feel Your
Pulse*. New York: Doubleday, Page, & Co., 1910. First
ed. Light-brown publisher's cloth with paper illustration pasted on front. Readers still delight in O. Henry's
"humor humanism, and the classic 'O. Henry Twist'"
(ANB) that somehow, even in the most somber of stories, manages a happy ending. PW noted that "this is
the last story O. Henry wrote, and it is probably his
best. It has all his subtle and broad fun. If you have a
nerve-sick friend, throw him this life line to cheerful-
ness" (PW, Nov. 26, 1910, p. 81). American Firsts, p.
420; BAL 16296; Clarkson, p. 54.

Works Cited

Adler, Betty. *H.L.M.: The Mencken Bibliography*. Compiled by Betty Adler with the assistance of Jane Williams. John Hopkins Press, 1961.

Armstrong, Margaret. *Fanny Kemble: A Passionate Victorian*. Macmillan, 1938.

Atkinson, Jennifer McCabe. *Eugene O'Neill: A Descriptive Bibliography*. University of Pittsburgh Press, 1974.

Basbanes, Nicholas A. "Collectors and Libraries: Some Studies in Symbiosis." *Rare Books and Manuscripts Librarianship* vol. 8, no. 1, 1993, pp. 37–48.

Battiscombe, Georgina. *Charlotte Mary Yonge: The Story of an Uneventful Life*. Constable & Co., 1943.

Beasley, Jerry C. *A Check List of Prose Fiction Published in England, 1740–1749*. Bibliographical Society of the University of Virginia, 1972.

Bendixen, Alfred, & Stephen Burt, eds. *The Cambridge History of American Poetry*. Cambridge University Press, 2015.

Black, Frank Gees. *The Epistolary Novel in the Late Eighteenth Century. A Descriptive and Bibliographical Study*. University of Oregon, 1940.

Blanck, Jacob. *Bibliography of American Literature*. Yale University Press, 1955–1990. 9 vols.

Blanck, Jacob. *Merle Johnson's American First Editions*. Fourth ed. R.R. Bowker, 1942.

Blanck, Jacob. *Peter Parley to Penrod: A Bibliographical Description of the Best-Loved American Juvenile Books*. Mark Press, 1974.

Block, Andrew. *The English Novel, 1740–1850*. Dowsons of Pall Mall, 1961.

Bonnell, F.W., & F.C. Bonnell. *Conrad Aiken: A Bibliography, 1902–1978*. Huntington Library, 1982.

Brack, O.M., & Leslie A. Chilton, eds. *The Adventures of Gil Blas of Santillane.* Tobias Smollett, trans. University of Georgia Press, 2011.

British Library. *English Short Title Catalogue* [online]. British Library, 2020. http://estc.bl.uk

Brussel, I.R. *Anglo-American First Editions.* R.R. Bowker, 1935–1936.

Bryant, William Cullen. *A Discourse on the Life, Character and Genius of Washington Irving.* G.P. Putnam, 1860.

Buckley, Matthew. "Sensations of Celebrity: Jack Sheppard and the Mass Audience." *Victorian Studies* vol. 44, no. 3, 2002, pp. 423–463.

Cahoon, Herbert. *Herman Melville: A Check List of Books and Manuscripts in the Collections of the New York Public Library.* New York Public Library, 1951.

Cambridge University Press. *The Rothschild Library: A Catalogue of the Collection of Eighteenth-Century Printed Books and Manuscripts Formed by Lord Rothschild.* Cambridge University Press, 1954.

Carr, Lucile. *A Catalogue of the Vander Poel Dickens Collection at the University of Texas.* University of Texas at Austin, 1968.

Castiglia, Christopher, & Glenn Hendler, eds. *Franklin Evans, or The Inebriate: A Tale of the Times*, by Walt Whitman. Duke University Press, 2007.

Chambers, M. Clark. *Kay Boyle: A Bibliography.* Oak Knoll Press, 2002.

Chapman, Guy. *A Bibliography of William Beckford of Fonthill.* Constable & Co., 1930.

Charters, Ann. *A Bibliography of Works by Jack Kerouac.* Phoenix Book Shop, 1967.

Clark, C.E. Frazer. *Nathaniel Hawthorne: A Descriptive Bibliography.* University of Pittsburgh Press, 1978.

Clarkson, Paul S. *A Bibliography of William Sydney Porter (O. Henry).* Caxton Printers, 1938.

Cohn, Albert M. *A Bibliographical Catalogue of the Printed Works Illustrated by George Cruickshank.* Longmans, Green, and Co., 1914.

Cohn, Albert M. *George Cruikshank, A Catalogue Raisonne of the Work Executed During the Years 1806–1877.* Bookman's Journal, 1924.

Connolly, Cyril. *The Modern Movement: One Hundred Key Books from England, France and America 1880–1950.* Atheneum, 1966.

Courtney, William Prideaux. *A Bibliography of Samuel Johnson.* Clarendon Press, 1925.

Cowan, Robert Ernest, & William Andrews Clark, Jr. *The Library of William Andrews Clark, Jr.: Modern English Literature.* Vol. 1. Printed by John Henry Nash, 1920.

Craigie, Dorothy M. *Victorian Detective Fiction: A Catalogue of the Collection Made by Dorothy Glover & Graham Greene.* Bodley Head, 1966.

Crandell, George W. *Tennessee Williams A Descriptive Bibliography.* University of Pittsburgh Press, 1995.

Crane, Joan St. C. *Robert Frost: A Descriptive Catalogue of Books and Manuscripts in the Clifton Waller Barrett Library, University of Virginia.* University Press of Virginia, 1974.

Cross, Robert, & Anna Ravenscroft-Hulme. *Vita Sackville-West: A Bibliography.* Oak Knoll Press, 1999.

Crowley, John W. *The Dean of American Letters.* University of Massachusetts Press, 1999.

Currier, Thomas Franklin, & Eleanor M. Tilton. *A Bibliography of Oliver Wendell Holmes.* New York University Press, 1953.

Currier, Thomas Franklin. *A Bibliography of John Greenleaf Whittier.* Harvard University Press, 1937.

Cutler, B.D. *Sir James M. Barrie, A Bibliography.* Greenberg, 1931.

Davis, Robert Murray, et al. *Evelyn Waugh: A Checklist of Primary and Secondary Material.* Whitston, 1972.

DeSalvo, Louise, & Mitchell A. Leaska, eds. *The Letters of Vita Sackville-West to Virginia Woolf.* Morrow, 1985.

Donaldson, Scott. *Archibald MacLeish: An American Life.* Houghton Mifflin, 1992.

Eagleton, Terry. *Literary Theory: An Introduction.* University of Minnesota Press, 2003.

Eckel, John C. *The First Editions of the Writings of Charles Dickens and Their Values: A Bibliography.* Chapman & Hall, 1913.

Edel, Leon, & Dan H. Laurence. *A Bibliography of Henry James.* Third ed. Clarendon Press, 1982.

Egerer, J.W. "Fales Library." *Stechert-Hafner Book News* vol. 19, no. 2, 1964.

Egerer, J.W. *A Bibliography of Robert Burns.* Oliver & Boyd, 1964.

Egerer, J.W. *DeCoursey Fales, 1888–1966.* New York University Libraries, 1966.

Ellis, Stewart Marsh. *William Harrison Ainsworth and His Friends.* John Lane, 1911.

Emery, Norman. *Arnold Bennett (1867–1931): A Bibliography.* Stoke-on-Trent Central Library, 1967.

Eschelbach, Claire John, & Joyce Lee Shober. *Aldous Huxley: A Bibliography, 1916–1959.* University of California Press, 1961.

Everett, Glenn. "A.C. Swinburne: Biography." *Victorian Web.* http://www.victorianweb.org/authors/swinburne/acsbio1.html

Fales, DeCoursey. *Confessions of a Book Collector.* Privately printed, 1960.

Federman, Raymond, & John Fletcher. *Samuel Beckett: His Works and His Critics, An Essay In Bibliography.* University of California Press, 1970.

Fleeman, J.D. *A Bibliography of the Works of Samuel Johnson: Treating His Published Works from the Beginnings to 1984.* Oxford University Press, 2000.

Gallatin, A.E., & L.M. Oliver. *A Bibliography of the Works of Max Beerbohm*. Harvard University Press, 1952.

Gallup, Donald. *T.S. Eliot: A Bibliography*. Faber & Faber, 1969.

Garland, Herbert. *A Bibliography of the Writings of Sir James Matthew Barrie*. Bookman's Journal, 1928.

Garrison, Stephen. *Edith Wharton: A Descriptive Bibliography*. University of Pittsburgh Press, 1990.

Garside, Peter, et al. *The English Novel 1770–1829: A Bibliographical Survey of Prose Fiction published in the British Isles*. Oxford University Press, 2000.

Gibson, William M., & George Arms. *A Bibliography of William Dean Howells*. New York Public Library, 1948.

Gilbert, Colleen B. *A Bibliography of the Works of Dorothy L. Sayers*. Archon, 1978.

Goldstone, Adrian H., & John R. Payne. *John Steinbeck: A Bibliographical Catalogue of the Adrian H. Goldstone Collection*. University of Texas at Austin, 1974.

Gordon, John D. *Arnold Bennett, The Centenary of His Birth: An Exhibition in the Berg Collection*. New York Public Library, 1967.

Gordon, John D. *Bernard Shaw, 1856–1950: An Exhibition from the Berg Collection*. New York Public Library, 1956.

Green, Richard Lancelyn, & John Michael Gibson. *A Bibliography of A. Conan Doyle*. Clarendon Press, 1983.

Green, Roger L. *Andrew Lang: A Critical Biography with a Short-Title Bibliography of the Works of Andrew Lang*. Edmund Ward, 1946.

Grolier Club. *One Hundred Books Famous in English Literature*. Grolier Club, 1902.

Grolier Club. *One Hundred Influential American Books Printed Before 1900: Catalogue and Addresses*. Grolier Club, 1947.

Gulliver, Lucile. *Louisa May Alcott: A Bibliography*. Little, Brown, & Co., 1932.

Healey, George Harris. *The Cornell Wordsworth Collection: A Catalogue of Books and Manuscripts Presented to the University by Mr. Victor Emanuel.* Cornell University Press, 1957.

Heinemann, James H., & Donald R. Bensen, eds. *P.G. Wodehouse: A Centaury Celebration, 1881–1981.* Oxford University Press, 1981.

Higginson, A. Henry. *British and American Sporting Authors: Their Writings and Biographies.* Blue Ridge Press, 1949.

Higginson, Fred H. *A Bibliography of the Writings of Robert Graves.* Second ed. revised by William Proctor Williams. St. Paul's Bibliographies, 1987.

Hildreth, Margaret Holbrook. *Harriet Beecher Stowe A Bibliography.* Archon, 1976.

Hilles, Frederick Whiley. *The Literary Career of Sir Joshua Reynolds.* Cambridge University Press, 1936.

Hogan, Charles Beecher. *A Bibliography of Edwin Arlington Robinson.* Yale University Press, 1936.

Holmes, Thomas James. *The Minor Mathers: A List of their Works.* Harvard University Press, 1940.

Jackson, Holbrook. *The Eighteen Nineties.* Jonathan Cape, 1927.

Jackson, Joseph. *A Bibliography of the Works of George Lippard.* Historical Society of Pennsylvania, 1930.

Jasen, David A. *A Bibliography and Reader's Guide to the First Editions of P.G. Wodehouse.* Archon, 1970.

Johnson, Edgar. *Sir Walter Scott in the Fales Library.* New York University Libraries, 1968.

Johnson, Merle. *A Bibliography of the Works of Mark Twain, Samuel Langhorne Clemens.* Harper & Brothers, 1910.

Johnson, Merle. *High Spots of American Literature.* Jenkins Publishing Company, 1971.

Jones, Dolores Blythe. *An "Oliver Optic" Checklist.* Greenwood Press, 1985.

Jones, Howard Mumford, ed. *English Traits*, by Ralph Waldo Emerson. Harvard University Press, 1966.

Joughin, G. Louis. *An Inchbald Bibliography*. University of Texas Press, 1934.

Keating, George T. *A Conrad Memorial Library*. Doubleday, Doran & Co., 1929.

Keynes, Geoffrey. *A Bibliography of Rupert Brooke*. Rupert Hart-Davis, 1959.

Keynes, Geoffrey. *A Bibliography of Siegfried Sassoon*. Rupert Hart-Davis, 1962.

Kherdian, David. *A Bibliography of William Saroyan, 1934–1964*. Roger Beacham, 1965.

Kirkpatrick, B.J. *A Bibliography of Virginia Woolf*. Revised edition. Rupert Hart-Davis, 1967.

Kramer, Sidney. *A History of Stone & Kimball and Herbert S. Stone & Co. With a Bibliography of Their Publications*. University of Chicago Press, 1940.

Kunitz, Stanley J., & Howard Haycraft, eds. *British Authors of the Nineteenth Century*. H.W. Wilson, 1964.

Labor, Earle, ed. *The Portable Jack London*. Penguin, 1994.

Langfield, William R. *Washington Irving: A Bibliography*. New York Public Library, 1933.

Laurence, Dan H. *Bernard Shaw: A Bibliography*. Clarendon Press, 1983.

Le Gallienne, Richard. *The Romantic '90s*. G.P. Putnam's Sons, 1926.

Littlewood, S.W. *Elizabeth Inchbald and Her Circle: The Life Story of a Charming Woman, 1753–1821*. Daniel O'Connor, 1921.

Livingston, Flora V. *Bibliography of the Works of Rudyard Kipling*. Edgar H. Wells & Co., 1927.

Livingston, Luther Samuel. *A Bibliography of the First Editions in Book Form of the Writings of Alfred, Lord Tennyson*. Dodd, Mead & Co., 1901.

Livingston, Luther Samuel. *A Bibliography of the First Editions in Book Form of the Writings of Henry Wadsworth Longfellow.* Privately printed, 1908.

Livingston, Luther Samuel. *A Bibliography of the First Editions in Book Form of the Writings of James Russell Lowell.* Privately printed, 1914.

Locke, Harold. *A Bibliographical Catalogue of the Published Novels and Ballads of William Harrison Ainsworth.* Elkin Mathews, 1925.

Loeber, Rolf, & Magda Loeber. *A Guide to Irish Fiction, 1650–1900.* Four Courts Press, 2006.

Lofts, W.O.G., & Derek Adley. *The British Bibliography of Edgar Wallace.* Howard Baker, 1969.

Luckett, Perry D. *Charles A. Lindbergh: A Bio-Bibliography.* Greenwood Press, 1986.

Marrot, H.V. *A Bibliography of the Works of John Galsworthy.* Burt Franklin, 1968.

Mason, Stuart. *Bibliography of Oscar Wilde.* Bertram Rota, 1967.

Massey, Linton R. *William Faulkner: "Man Working," 1919–1962: A Catalogue of the William Faulkner Collections at the University of Virginia.* University Press of Virginia, 1968.

May, James Lewis. *John Lane and the Nineties.* John Lane, 1936.

McDonald, Edward D. *A Bibliography of the Writings of Theodore Dreiser.* Centaur Book Shop, 1928.

McKay, George L. *A Stevenson Library: A Catalogue of a Collection of Writings by and About Robert Louis Stevenson formed by Edwin J. Beinecke.* Yale University Library, 1951.

Metzdorf, Robert F. *The Tinker Library: A Bibliographical Catalogue of the Books and Manuscripts Collected by Chauncey Brewster Tinker.* Yale University Library, 1959.

Miller, George, & Hugoe Matthews. *Richard Jefferies: A Bibliographical Study*. Scolar Press, 1993.

Miller, Robert H. *Graham Greene A Descriptive Catalog*. University Press of Kentucky, 1979.

Minnigerode, Meade. *Some Personal Letters of Herman Melville and a Bibliography*. Books for Libraries Press, 1969.

Mizener, Arthur. *A Catalogue of The First Editions of Archibald MacLeish*. Yale University Library, 1938.

Myerson, Joel. *Ralph Waldo Emerson: A Descriptive Bibliography*. University of Pittsburgh Press, 1982.

Nelson, James G. *The Early Nineties: A View from the Bodley Head*. Cambridge: Harvard University Press, 1971.

New York University. "Dinner for DeCoursey Fales." Memorandum from "SS" (Office of the President) to unknown recipient, undated. The dinner was scheduled for Dec. 18, 1957.

Nicoll, Allardyce. *A History of Late Eighteenth-Century Drama, 1750–1800*. Vol. 3. Cambridge University Press, 1927.

Osborne, Charles. *The Life and Crimes of Agatha Christie*. William Collins Sons & Co., 1982.

Oscar Lion Collection. *Walt Whitman: The Oscar Lion Collection*. New York Public Library, 1953.

Oxford University Press. *American National Biography* [online]. Oxford University Press, 2020.

Oxford University Press. *Oxford Dictionary of National Biography* [online]. Oxford University Press, 2020.

Parke-Bernet Galleries. *The Edward Hubert Litchfield Collection of First Editions of English & American Authors, Incunabula and Other Early Books*. Parke-Bernet Galleries, 1951.

Parrish, Morris L. *A List of the Writings of Lewis Carroll in the Library at Dormy House, Pine Valley, New Jersey*. Privately printed, 1928.

Parrish, Morris L. *Victorian Lady Novelists*. Burt Franklin, 1969.

Parrish, Morris L. *Wilkie Collins and Charles Reade*. Constable & Co., 1940.

Pastore, Stephen R. *Sinclair Lewis: A Descriptive Bibliography*. University of Scranton Press, 2009.

Patterson, Michael. *The Oxford Dictionary of Plays*. Oxford University Press, 2005.

Peck, Louis F. *A Life of Matthew G. Lewis*. Harvard University Press, 1961.

Perry, Bliss. *A Study of Prose Fiction*. Houghton, Mifflin, 1902.

Phillips, Rodney, et al. *The Hand of the Poet: Poems and Papers in Manuscript*. Rizzoli, 1997.

Podeschi, John B. *Dickens and Dickensiana*. Yale University Library, 1980.

Potter, Jack. *A Bibliography of John Dos Passos*. Normandie House, 1950.

Prideaux, W.F. *A Bibliography of the Works of Robert Louis Stevenson*. Burt Franklin, 1968.

Princeton University Library. *Robert Louis Stevenson: A Catalogue of the Henry E. Gerstely Stevenson Collection, the Stevenson Section of the Morris L. Parrish Collection of Victorian Novelists, and Items From Other Collection in the Department of Rare Books and Special Collections of the Princeton University Library*. Princeton University Library, 1971.

Purdy, Richard Little. *Thomas Hardy: A Bibliographical Study*. Oak Knoll Press, 2002.

Raven, James. *British Fiction, 1750–1770: A Chronological Check-List of Prose Fiction Printed in Britain and Ireland*. University of Delaware Press and Associated University Presses, 1987.

Reed, Mark L. *A Bibliography of William Wordsworth, 1787–1930*. Cambridge University Press, 2013.

Richards, David Allen. *Rudyard Kipling: A Bibliography*. Oak Knoll Press, 2010.

Roberts, Warren, & Paul Poplawski. *A Bibliography of D.H. Lawrence*. Third ed. Cambridge University Press, 2001.

Robinson, Forrest G. Afterword to *Merry Tales*, by Mark Twain (Shelley Fisher Fishkin, ed.). Oxford University Press, 1996.

Rodgers, Marion Elizabeth. *Mencken: The American Iconoclast*. Oxford University Press, 2005.

Russo, Dorothy Ritter, & Thelma L. Sullivan. *A Bibliography of Booth Tarkington, 1869–1946*. Indiana Historical Society, 1949.

Sadleir, Michael. *Trollope: A Bibliography*. Constable & Co., 1928.

Sadleir, Michael. *XIX Century Fiction: A Bibliographical Record Based on His Own Collection*. Cooper Square Publishers, 1969.

Samuels Lasner, Mark. *A Selective Checklist of the Published Work of Aubrey Beardsley*. Thomas G. Boss, 1995.

Sanders, David. *John Dos Passos A Comprehensive Bibliography*. Garland, 1987.

Scharnhorst, Gary. *Bret Harte A Bibliography*. Scarecrow Press, 1995.

Schlicke, Paul, ed. *Oxford Reader's Companion to Dickens*. Oxford University Press, 1999.

Schrader, Richard J. *H.L. Mencken A Descriptive Bibliography*. University of Pittsburgh Press, 1998.

Schwartz, Edward. *Katherine Anne Porter A Critical Bibliography*. New York Public Library, 1953.

Scofield, Martin. *The Cambridge Introduction to the American Short Story*. Cambridge University Press, 2006.

Shifreen, Laurence J., & Roger Jackson. *Henry Miller: A Bibliography of primary sources*. L.J. Shifreen & R. Jackson, 1993.

Shillinglaw, Susan. Back cover of *Cannery Row*, by John Steinbeck. Penguin Books, 1994.

Slade, Bertha Coolidge. *Maria Edgeworth, 1767–1849: A Bibliographical Tribute*. Constable, 1937.

Slocum, John J., & Herbert Cahoon. *A Bibliography of James Joyce*. Yale University Press, 1953.

Smith, Harrison, ed. *From Main Street to Stockholm: Letters of Sinclair Lewis, 1919–1930*. Harcourt, Brace & Co., 1952.

Smith, Walter E. *Joseph Conrad: A Bibliographical Catalogue of His Major First Editions with Facsimiles of Several Title Pages*. Privately printed, 1979

Spiller, Robert E., & Philip C. Blackburn. *A Descriptive Bibliography of the Writings of James Fenimore Cooper*. Burt Franklin, 1968.

Stallman, R.W. *Stephen Crane: A Critical Bibliography*. Iowa State University Press, 1972.

Stannard, Martin. *Evelyn Waugh: The Early Years, 1903–1939*. J.M. Dent & Sons, 1986.

Starett, Vincent. *Stephen Crane: A Bibliography*. Centaur Book Shop, 1923.

Stevenson, Lionel. *The Wild Irish Girl: The Life of Sydney Owenson, Lady Morgan (1776–1859)*. Russell & Russell, 1969.

Stewart, James McGregor, & A.W. Yeats. *Rudyard Kipling: A Bibliographical Catalogue*. Dalhousie University Press, 1959.

Stirling, Monica. *The Fine and the Wicked: The Life and Times of Ouida*. Victor Gollancz, 1958.

Suarez, Michael F., & H.R. Woudhuysen, eds. *The Oxford Companion to the Book*. Oxford University Press, 2010.

Sullivan, John. *G.K. Chesterton A Bibliography*. University of London Press, 1958.

Summers, Montague. *A Gothic Bibliography*. Russell & Russell, 1965.

Symington, J.A. *Bibliography of the Works of All Members of the Bronte Family and of Bronteana.* Ian Hodgkins & Co. and Oak Knoll Press, 2000.

Taylor, Marvin J., & Michael Kelly. *Facts and Fiction: The Fales Library and Special Collections at New York University.* New York University Libraries, 1999.

Todd, Janet, ed. *A Dictionary of British and American Woman Writers, 1660–1800.* Rowman & Littlefield, 1987.

Todd, William B., & Ann Bowden. *Sir Walter Scott: A Bibliographical History, 1796–1832.* Oak Knoll Press, 1998.

Van Duzer, Henry Sayre. *A Thackeray Library: First Editions and First Publications, Portraits, Water Colors, Etchings, Drawings and Manuscripts.* Privately printed, 1919.

Wade, Allan. *A Bibliography of the Writings of W.B. Yeats.* Rupert Hart-Davis, 1968.

Wagoner, Mary. *Tobias Smollett A Checklist of Editions of His Works and an Annotated Secondary Bibliography.* Garland, 1984.

Waldrip, Louise, & Shirley Ann Bauer. *A Bibliography of the Works of Katherine Anne Porter and A Bibliography of the Criticism of the Works of Katherine Anne Porter.* Scarecrow Press, 1969.

Watson, George, ed. *The New Cambridge Bibliography of English Literature.* Cambridge University Press, 1969–1977. 5 vols.

Weber, Clara Carter, & Carl J. Weber. *A Bibliography of the Published Writings of Sarah Orne Jewett.* Colby College Press, 1949.

Wells, Geoffrey H. *A Bibliography of the Works of H.G. Wells, 1898–1925.* Burt Franklin, 1968.

Wheelock, John Hall. *A Bibliography of Theodore Roosevelt.* Charles Scribner's Sons, 1920.

Whiteman, Maxwell. *A Century of Fiction by American Negroes.* Albert Saifer, 1968.

Williams, Sidney Herbert. *A Bibliography of the Writings of Lewis Carroll*. Bookman's Journal, 1924.

Wilson, Jean C.S., & David A. Randall, eds. *Carroll A. Wilson: Thirteen Author Collections of the Nineteenth Century and Five Centuries of Familiar Quotations*. Charles Scribner's Sons, 1950.

Wilt, Judith. "'All About the Heart': The Material-Theology of Maturin's *Melmoth the Wanderer*." In *The Fountain Light: Studies in Romanticism and Religion In Honor of John L. Mahoney* (J. Robert Barth, ed). Fordham University Press, 2002.

Winterich, John T. *The Fales Collection: A Record of Growth*. New York University Libraries, 1963.

Winterich, John T. *The Fales Collection: An Appreciation*. New York University Libraries, 1959.

Wise, Jon, & Mike Hill. *The Works of Graham Greene: A Reader's Bibliography and Guide*. Continuum, 2012.

Wise, Thomas James. *A Bibliography of the Writings in Prose and Verse of Algernon Charles Swinburne*. Privately printed, 1919–20.

Wise, Thomas James. *A Bibliography of the Writings in Prose and Verse of William Wordsworth*. Dawsons of Pall Mall, 1971.

Wise, Thomas James. *A Bibliography of the Writings of Alfred, Lord Tennyson*. Privately printed, 1908.

Wise, Thomas James. *A Bibliography of the Writings of Joseph Conrad (1895–1921)*. Dawsons of Pall Mall, 1964.

Wise, Thomas James. *Two Lake Poets: A Catalogue of Printed Books, Manuscripts and Autograph Letters by William Wordsworth and Samuel Taylor Coleridge*. Dawsons of Pall Mall, 1965.

Wobbe, R.A. *Graham Greene: A Bibliography and Guide to Research*. Garland, 1979.

Wolff, Robert Lee. *Nineteenth-Century Fiction: A Bibliographical Catalogue Based on the Collection Formed by Robert Lee Wolff*. Garland, 1981–86. 5 vols.

Woodbridge, Hensley C. *Jack London: A Bibliography*. Talisman Press, 1966.

Woolmer, J. Howard. *A Checklist of the Hogarth Press, 1917–1946*. Woolmer/Brotherson, 1986.

Worthington, Greville. *A Bibliography of the Waverly Novels*. Constable & Co., 1931.

Wright, Lyle Henry. *American Fiction, 1774–1850: A Contribution Toward a Bibliography*. Huntington Library, 1969.

Wright, Lyle Henry. *American Fiction, 1851–1875: A Contribution Toward a Bibliography*. Huntington Library, 1965.

Wright, Lyle Henry. *American Fiction, 1876–1900: A Contribution Toward a Bibliography*. Huntington Library, 1966.

Yablon, G. Anthony, & John R. Turner. *A Bronte Bibliography*. Ian Hodgkins & Co., 1978.

Made in the USA
Middletown, DE
27 June 2021